DIELECTRIC BEHAVIOR OF
PHYSICALLY ADSORBED GASES

DIELECTRIC BEHAVIOR OF
PHYSICALLY ADSORBED GASES

ROBERT L. McINTOSH

HEAD, DEPARTMENT OF CHEMISTRY
QUEEN'S UNIVERSITY
KINGSTON, ONTARIO, CANADA

1966

MARCEL DEKKER, Inc., New York

MARCEL DEKKER, INC.

95 Madison Avenue, New York, New York 10016

LIBRARY OF CONGRESS CATALOG CARD NUMBER 66-18430

PRINTED IN THE UNITED STATES OF AMERICA

To
Kitty, Alex, and Sharon
and
My Graduate Students

PREFACE

The dielectric properties of rigid gels, polymers, and crystal-line solids which have been allowed to adsorb gaseous matter have been examined many times. The aim of these studies has been the description of the properties of the adsorbed matter and the understanding of the forces which bring about the adsorption of the volatile component. Experimental techniques have been developed and improved until a wide choice of conditions has become available. Thus, a temperature range from well above the normal boiling point of many adsorbates to a temperature corresponding to the boiling point of liquid nitrogen has been made possible in conjunction with a frequency range from a few hundred cycles per second to thousands of megacycles per second. These developments have provided a large body of data which has led to the recognition of the completion of the first layer of adsorbate, a measure of bound water in proteins, and the activation energy of processes leading to dielectric loss, to mention a few of the contributions which have resulted from the studies. Unfortunately, less progress has been possible in describing the dielectric properties of the adsorbate itself. The reason for this is the difficult problem of the analysis of the internal fields which exist within the heterogeneous dielectrics. Thus, the relation between the macroscopic property of the composite dielectric and the molecular parameters of the adsorbed matter remains obscure.

In this review of the subject, I have attempted to keep an awareness of this difficulty before the reader. I have also tried to deal with those systems which have been most thoroughly investigated and which offer the best opportunity of allowing a quantitative interpretation of the experimental data. The presentation is therefore not comprehensive, although it is hoped that the selection of systems has been sufficiently broad to reveal the interest and value of this means of investigating the adsorbed state. The book is proffered with the hope that it will stimulate further work in the field, particularly by those who may resolve the problem of separating the dielectric properties of the adsorbate from those of the composite system more correctly. Such an advance would lead to a powerful means of investigating the gas-solid interface, since it has already been shown qualitatively that dielectric measurements reveal situations not readily observed by other familiar techniques.

Kingston, Ontario   R. L. McInTOSH
June, 1966

TABLE OF CONTENTS

CHAPTER 1

GENERAL INTRODUCTION

1-1 PROBLEMS INVOLVED

Since dielectric measurements combined with the theoretical work of Debye, Onsager, Fröhlich, Von Hippel, and others have led to significant advances in our understanding of the structure of molecules and of the liquid and solid states, application of these same methods to adsorbed films might also be expected to be advantageous. Generally speaking the theoretical background required is the same as for the study of solids and liquids. In this event no extensive review of the theory is

1

necessary, although special situations do require comment. Details of dielectric theory may be obtained from the excellent texts cited in the References.

Among the differences between gas-solid systems on the one hand and liquids or solids on the other is the important factor of heterogeneity. The heterogeneous gas-solid systems present difficulties on several counts. In the first instance the computation of the dielectric constant or polarization of either film or solid from that of the composite system poses problems not found for homogeneous systems. This aspect of the general problem is dealt with quite fully in Chapter 2. It need be said here only that either the methods of calculation recognize the heterogeneity or, because of the small particle size of solid samples ordinarily used, the assumption is made that the formulas for homogeneous solutions may be employed.

Heterogeneity of the systems on a much smaller scale is also important. The environment of the species of interest, namely, the adsorbed gas, is not uniform. If the usual concepts of physical-adsorption theory are retained, one supposes that the adsorbed molecule lies in the field emanating from the solid and that at low surface concentrations its behavior will be governed by the nature of the solid surface. There is much evidence to demonstrate the physically and energetically heterogeneous nature of the solid surface. Even in the unrealizable case of an ideal ionic surface, account must be taken of the periodic field of force.

From the experimental standpoint difficulties arise because of the small amount of matter which is being subjected to examination. The amount of adsorbed gas is small in comparison with the amount of solid, and this makes precise measurements mandatory. More serious, however, is the theoretical question of whether the change of dielectric properties is to be attributed to the adsorbate alone or to the adsorbent also. An interesting case, which illustrates the difficulty, arose with ethyl chloride adsorbed on porous glass (*1*)* (see Figure 5-2). At a low temperature the total capacity of glass plus adsorbate was found to be less than the capacity when glass alone was in the cell. If the usual method is adopted of expressing thermodynamic quantities for physically adsorbed gases, the difficulty is immediately obvious. It will be recalled that the property of the adsorbate is considered by Hill to be that of the total system less that of the pure solid in the same state of subdivision at the same temperature and under the same hydrostatic pressure (*2*). Application of this practice to the system glass–ethyl chloride is clearly not possible. Unless, however, some such situation is found, the increment of capacity of the test cell from that without adsorbate is considered to be due to the adsorbate and the solid is assumed to be inert.

Among the questions to which one would like an answer concerning the behavior of the adsorbed matter are the following: Does the molecule turn freely at the adsorption site? Does the molecule lie in a potential energy well, and will its motion therefore resemble that of a rotational or vibrational oscillator? What is the natural frequency of the motion of the molecule? Is the heterogeneity of the surface recognizable through the apparent moment or the frequency of the motion or both? Does interaction with its neighbors influence the behavior of the molecule noticeably? Can the properties of the molecules in the first layer be distinguished from the properties of those in higher layers?

In later chapters the measure of success which has been achieved in dealing with these questions is outlined. It is now useful to give an indication as to how dielectric theory can help in their resolution.

*Italic numerals on the line in parentheses correspond to the numbers of the References at the end of each chapter.

1-2 APPLICATIONS OF THE DEBYE EQUATIONS

Debye's theory of the relationship between polarization and dielectric constant is expressed through the relationship $(\varepsilon - 1)/4\pi = N(\alpha + \mu^2/3kT)(\varepsilon + 2)/3$, where α is a molecular constant giving the distortion polarizability of the molecule and μ is the value of the permanent moment. The factor $(\varepsilon + 2)/3$ arises from the Clausius-Mosotti relation between the internal field at the molecule and the applied field across the dielectric. Provided, then, that the Clausius-Mosotti relationship holds, a measurement of the dielectric constant of the adsorbate would appear to lead to the moment of the adsorbed molecule. However, Debye's relationship is valid only at low frequencies of the measuring field and for circumstances in which the potential energy of the dipole in the field is expressed by $\mu E_r \cos \theta$, where θ is the angle between the direction of the dipole and the directing field E_r. Upon leaving aside, then, any questions concerning the validity of the Clausius-Mosotti field, there are two factors which must be considered, namely, the validity of the Debye expression for the potential energy of the adsorbed molecule and the effect of frequency upon dielectric constant.

Kurbatov (3) first showed that the contribution $\mu^2 E_r/3kT$ of the permanent dipoles to the orientational polarization is modified if the dipole is an oscillator. He obtained the relation $\bar{m} = 2\mu^2 E_r/3I\omega_0^2$, where ω_0 is the frequency of oscillation for a molecule making small oscillations in three dimensions and I is the moment of inertia. He also showed that a molecule free to rotate within a cone of angle $2\theta_0$ but constrained to rotate within that cone has an orientational moment $\bar{m} = \mu^2 E_r [1 - \cos^4 (\theta_0/2)]/3kT$. McIntosh and co-workers (4) examined the case of a dipole free to rotate in a plane which might take any orientation with respect to the applied field and showed that $\bar{m} = \mu^2 E_r/3kT$. Channen and McIntosh (5) corrected an error made by Snelgrove and McIntosh (6) and showed that a rigid molecule undergoing rotational oscillations in a plane parallel to the surface, and for which the midpoints of the oscillations were randomly oriented within the plane, yielded $\bar{m} = \mu^2 E_r/3I\omega_0^2$. The two interesting features of the formulas for oscillators are, first, that the variation of $\bar{m}$ with temperature becomes negligible and, second, that the contribution to the polarization of the permanent moments is always appreciably less than would be anticipated on the basis of the gaseous moment.

Both these conclusions warrant comment along the lines employed by Channen (7).

The polarization of the adsorbed matter may be written

$$\mathbf{E}_2(\varepsilon_2 - 1)/4\pi = N(\alpha\mathbf{E}_{i_2} + \overline{\mathbf{m}}) = N[\alpha\mathbf{E}_{i_2} + (\bar{m}/E_{r_2})\mathbf{E}_{r_2}] \quad (1\text{-}1)$$

where $\mathbf{E}_2$ is the macroscopic field in the adsorbate, $\mathbf{E}_{i_2}$ and $\mathbf{E}_{r_2}$, respectively, are the total internal and directing fields at the molecule, and $\overline{\mathbf{m}}$ is the average value of the permanent dipole in the direction of the applied field. For low field intensities $\mathbf{E}_{i_2}$ and $\mathbf{E}_{r_2}$ are both functions of ε_2 and of the dielectric constant of the surrounding solid. Assuming that the influence of the solid does not vary with temperature, we may write

$$\mathbf{E}_{i_2} = f(\varepsilon_2)\mathbf{E}_2 \quad (1\text{-}2)$$

and

$$\mathbf{E}_{r_2} = g(\varepsilon_2)\mathbf{E}_2 \quad (1\text{-}3)$$

so that

$$[1/g(\varepsilon_2)][(\varepsilon_2 - 1)/(4\pi N) - \alpha f(\varepsilon_2)] = \bar{m}/E_{r_2} \quad (1\text{-}4)$$

In the case of polar gases $\bar{m}/E_r = \mu^2/3kT$ and the left-hand side would be a function of temperature so that ε_2 would vary with temperature. In the case of the rotational oscillator, however, $\bar{m}/E_r = \mu^2/3I\omega_0^2$, which implies that ε_2 is independent of temperature. The sensitivity of the temperature dependence of ε_2

depends upon the forms of the functions $f(\varepsilon_2)$ and $g(\varepsilon_2)$, and these are not known. Nevertheless the implication exists that ε_2 may be invariant with temperature.

The expression $\bar{m}/E_r = \mu^2/3I\omega_0^2$ was obtained by taking the first term of a power series, as is shown in Appendix B, where this case is worked out as an illustration. This is accurate for $\beta^2 \geqslant 10$ and is accurate within a few per cent for $\beta^2 > 1$. If $\beta^2 = 1$ and molecular constants for hydrogen chloride are used to evaluate I, ω_0 has a value of about 5×10^{12} per sec, which is the correct order of magnitude. For this case $\bar{m}$ for an oscillator has the value $\mu^2 E_r \times 4.5 \times 10^{12}$, while under the same conditions a Debye type of rotator has the value $\mu^2 E_r \times 12 \times 10^{12}$. Thus, even for comparatively small binding forces acting upon the adsorbed molecule, the contribution from it to orientational polarization is less than for a gaseous molecule.

A particular model of a rotational oscillator with molecular properties similar to those of hydrogen chloride has been fully treated by Benson and colleagues (8). The surface chosen was the (100) face of a sodium chloride crystal. The detailed examination of this model confirmed the conclusions stated above, namely, that the variation of ε_2 with temperature should be negligible and that the contribution of the permanent dipole to the orientational polarization should be much less than that anticipated from a knowledge of the gaseous moment.

In the same paper a discussion is given concerning the effect of dipoles induced by the field of the surface. Even in the case of a molecule like that described, but which rotates freely in the presence of the field (a physically unrealistic model), an induced moment of half the gaseous moment increases the apparent moment only by about 3 per cent. The importance of these remarks is to emphasize the small likelihood of apparent moments of adsorbed molecules being greater than gaseous moments. Should a larger moment be found, suspicion is cast upon the correctness of the formula used to evaluate the polarization.

1-3 EFFECT OF FREQUENCY ON DIELECTRIC CONSTANTS

Debye (9) and Fröhlich (10) have shown that the effect of frequency may be expressed as

$$(\varepsilon' - \varepsilon_\infty)/(\varepsilon_s - \varepsilon_\infty) = 1/(1 + \omega^2\tau^2) \tag{1-5}$$

$$\varepsilon''/(\varepsilon_s - \varepsilon_\infty) = \omega\tau/(1 + \omega^2\tau^2) \tag{1-6}$$

where ε' and ε'' are the real and imaginary parts of the complex dielectric constant. Fröhlich in particular has emphasized that these equations are valid for any system which approaches its equilibrium polarization exponentially and with a single relaxation time. He has shown that the Debye equations result also from a system of dipoles with two equilibrium orientations of equal energy when no field is applied and for which an activation energy must be acquired to permit rotation from one equilibrium position to the other. A distribution of relaxation times broadens the curve of ε'' against frequency. An important object of any experimentation, therefore, is to ascertain whether or not the Debye relations obtain. This includes the variation of ε' with temperature in the low-frequency region and the variation of ε' and ε'' with frequency in the region of power absorption, as well as their dependence upon temperature.

Fröhlich established a general formula for the dependence of polarization upon the frequency of the applied field (11). The expression is

$$D(t) = \varepsilon_\infty E(t) + \int_0^t E(u)\alpha(t - u)\, du \tag{1-7}$$

where $D(t)$ is the displacement at time t, $E(t)$ the value of the field at t, and $E(u)$ the value of the time-dependent field initiated at $u = 0$. The displacement D is not necessarily in phase with E and may thus be expressed through the complex dielectric constant and field as $\varepsilon(E)$. The term $\alpha(t - u)$ is the function describing the decay of the polarization with time. For periodic fields, an equation

$$\varepsilon(\omega) = \varepsilon_\infty + \int_0^\infty \alpha(x)e^{-j\omega x}\, dx \qquad (1\text{-}8)$$

may be written for the complex dielectric constant as a function of frequency where $x = t - u$. Combining with this expression the function

$$\alpha(t) = \gamma\, e^{-t/\tau} \cos(\omega_0 t + \psi) \qquad (1\text{-}9)$$

for a system of damped oscillators leads, as Fröhlich has shown, to the expressions

$$\varepsilon' - \varepsilon_\infty = \tfrac{1}{2}(\varepsilon_s - \varepsilon_\infty)\{[1 + \omega_0(\omega + \omega_0)\tau^2]/[1 + (\omega + \omega_0)^2\tau^2]$$
$$+ [1 - \omega_0(\omega - \omega_0)\tau^2]/[1 + (\omega - \omega_0)^2\tau^2]\} \qquad (1\text{-}10)$$

and

$$\varepsilon'' = \tfrac{1}{2}(\varepsilon_s - \varepsilon_\infty)\{\omega\tau/[1 + (\omega + \omega_0)^2\tau^2]$$
$$+ \omega\tau/[1 + (\omega - \omega_0)^2\tau^2]\} \qquad (1\text{-}11)$$

where ω_0 is the natural frequency of the oscillators and τ is the relaxation time.

On introducing the equation of motion of an assembly of damped oscillators in (1-8) the expressions for ε' and ε'' are deduced as functions of frequency and of temperature. In this development no assumption is made concerning the internal field, since the dielectric is considered to be homogeneous and the relationship between field and polarization is expressed in terms of the applied field. Application of these expressions to the systems under discussion necessitates an evaluation of the polarization of the adsorbate. The importance of this expression, which describes the absorption of a resonant system, is clear in view of the possibility of the existence of rotational oscillators. See Chapter 3.

The theoretical background which has been outlined is the structure presently available upon which an analysis of the behavior of the adsorbed molecule must be based. In the present state of uncertainty concerning the correct procedures of deriving polarizations, no attention has been paid to questions of shape or geometric arrangement of adsorbate within the structure.

REFERENCES

1. I. Chapman and R. McIntosh, *Can. J. Chem.*, **40**, 92 (1962).

2. T. L. Hill, *J. Chem. Phys.*, **18**, 246 (1950).

3. L. N. Kurbatov, *Russian J. Phys. Chem. (English Trans.)*, **24**, 899 (1950)

4. R. McIntosh, E. K. Rideal, and J. A. Snelgrove, *Proc. Roy. Soc. (London)*, **A208**, 292 (1951).

5. E. W. Channen and R. McIntosh, *Can. J. Chem.*, **33**, 172 (1955).

6. J. A. Snelgrove and R. McIntosh, *Can. J. Chem.*, **31**, 84 (1953).

7. E. W. Channen, Thesis, University of Toronto, 1956.

8. G. C. Benson, E. W. Channen, and R. McIntosh, *J. Colloid Sci.*, **11**, 593 (1956).

9. P. Debye, "Polar Molecules," p. 77ff., Chemical Catalog Company, Inc., New York, 1929.

10. H. Fröhlich, "Theory of Dielectrics: Dielectric Constant and Dielectric Loss," pp. 70ff., Oxford University Press, New York, 1949.

11. H. Fröhlich, "Theory of Dielectrics: Dielectric Constant and Dielectric Loss," pp. 7ff., Clarendon Press, Oxford, 1949.

CHAPTER 2

THE CALCULATION OF

POLARIZATION OF THE ADSORBATE

2-1 COMPUTATION OF DIELECTRIC VALUES

In the case of gas-solid systems, the initial problem is the evaluation of the polarization of the adsorbed material. This is more complicated than for homogeneous systems. In the latter case the requirement is to relate the measured polarization to the molecular properties of the individual molecules. The difficulty, as is well known, comes from the unknown value of the field acting at the position of the molecule. In the gas-solid systems, the first step must be to obtain a correct assessment of the polarization of the adsorbate. Thereafter the problem becomes the standard one of relating polarization to molecular properties. It cannot be claimed that a satisfactory solution of the primary difficulty has been achieved; in the following section an attempt is made to clarify the assumptions underlying each of the various procedures and to compare the treatments.

2-2 THE DIELECTRIC CONSTANT OF CRYSTALLINE POWDERS

A. Introduction

Since the systems usually examined experimentally consist either of finely divided solids and adsorbed gas or of granules of porous solid and adsorbed gas, an introduction to the methods of computation may be made in terms of the procedures used with crystalline powders. The subject is more fully reviewed by Böttcher (1).

On the assumption that the internal field at every point is correctly given by $(\varepsilon + 2)/3$ times the macroscopic field and that polarization is considered additive upon a volume-fraction basis, the formula $(\varepsilon - 1)/(\varepsilon + 2) = \delta_1(\varepsilon_1 - 1)/(\varepsilon_1 + 2)$ is deduced and has been found inadequate (1). Wiener (2), Bruggeman (3), and others have contributed to the problem with some success, especially the latter, but the approach most readily adapted to heterogeneous adsorptive systems is that due to Böttcher (4). His procedure is outlined in the next paragraph, where explicit statement of the assumptions is made.

B. Böttcher's Powder Method

The development is based upon the following assumptions:
1. The average internal field in the heterogeneous dielectric,

and in any phase thereof, is given by the factor $(\varepsilon + 2)/3$ times the macroscopic field. ε is the appropriate dielectric constant.

2. The average internal field is given by the addition of the individual internal fields on a volume-fraction basis.

3. The over-all polarization of the composite system is also given by adding the individual polarizations on a volume-fraction basis.

4. The polarization of each phase is related to its volume-average polarizability by the relation $P_i = C_i E_i$, where E_i is the average internal field of the ith phase.

5. The macroscopic field in voids or interstices is given by the usual formula for spherical voids, $E_3 = 3\varepsilon/(2\varepsilon + \varepsilon_3)$ times the applied field, where ε refers to the composite dielectric and ε_3 to the interstices.

On these bases

$$(\varepsilon + 2)E/3 = \delta_1 E_1 + \delta_3 E_3 \tag{2-1}$$

$$(\varepsilon - 1)E/4\pi = C_1 \delta_1 E_1 \tag{2-2}$$

Taking $\varepsilon_3 = 1$, one obtains

$$(\varepsilon + 2)/3 - 3\varepsilon\delta_3/(2\varepsilon + 1) = (\varepsilon - 1)/4\pi C_1 \tag{2-3}$$

which permits evaluation of C_1 and hence ε_1 from

$$(\varepsilon_1 - 1)/(\varepsilon_1 + 2) = \tfrac{4}{3}\pi C_1 \tag{2-4}$$

C. Kamiyoshi's Formula

Kamiyoshi (5) developed a formula based upon Rayleigh's result for spheres embedded in a dielectric. Kamiyoshi regarded the heterogeneous dielectric as spheres of dielectric constant ε_1 at the points of a cubic lattice in vacuum and as spherical voids at the points of a cubic lattice in a medium of dielectric constant ε_1,

$$E_1 = 1 - 3p/[(\varepsilon_1 + 2)/(\varepsilon_1 - 1) - p - 0.523p^{10/3}(\varepsilon_1 - 1)/(\varepsilon_1 + \tfrac{4}{3})] \tag{2-5}$$

is Rayleigh's result for the spheres in vacuum and

$$E_2 = \varepsilon_1 \{1 + 3p/[(2\varepsilon_1 + 1)/(\varepsilon_1 - 1) + p$$
$$- 0.523p^{10/3}(\varepsilon_1 - 1)/(\tfrac{4}{3}\varepsilon_1 + 1)]\} \quad (2\text{-}6)$$

the result for spherical voids in medium of constant ε_1. In both expressions p is volume fraction of dielectric of constant ε_1.

The average or over-all dielectric constant of the medium is given by

$$\varepsilon = (k + 1)E_1 E_2/(kE_1 + E_2) \quad (2\text{-}7)$$

In the case of nonporous solids k is given the value 1.0, but for porous solids its value must be obtained from a knowledge of the dielectric constant of the solid. Application of this formula to solids and adsorbed gases has been made by Ono et al. (*6*) and will be discussed in Section 6-4.

D. Cluster Method

It has been remarked that the formula of Kamiyoshi may contain an empirical constant for certain systems. Böttcher's method does not yield correct values for solids of high dielectric constant such as rutile, for which the average value of ε is given as 114 (*7*). Channen and McIntosh (*7*) attempted to correct the situation in the case of rutile. The known specific surface of the sample (about 85 m^2/g) indicated particles on the order of 10^{-6} cm in radius. In spite of this, powder particles were visible to the naked eye. Moreover, the volume fraction of solid in a lightly packed bed varied between 0.16 and 0.18, whereas normally powders exhibit a fraction of solid between 0.4 and 0.6. Both these facts are explicable if the ultimate particles form clusters which pack with space between clusters. In these circumstances one should compute the dielectric constant of a cluster from that of the composite dielectric, and then the value for a particle within the cluster. This was done for arbitrary values of the volume fractions within a cluster and of clusters within the assembly, subject to the condition that $\delta = \delta_i \delta_j$, where δ_i and δ_j are the two volume fractions. Excellent results were obtained for the value of solid rutile if the clusters were supposed to have a volume fraction of solid between that for cubic and that for hexagonal close packing for spheres. Alternatively, the packing of clusters within the bed could be assumed to be intermediate between that of cubic and hexagonal close packing.

This procedure is capable of extension to adsorbate-adsorbent systems as discussed in Section 5-3.

2-3 ADSORBATE-ADSORBENT SYSTEMS

A. Introduction

The extension of any of these treatments to adsorbate-adsorbent systems involves further assumptions. Even in the simplest case where additivity of dielectric constants on a volume-fraction basis is assumed, the value of ε_2 for the adsorbate is derived, but to make its value meaningful in terms of the physical behavior of the adsorbate requires comparison with the value for the bulk matter or its expression in terms of molecular parameters. In the first instance the usual assumption is that the adsorbate may be assumed to resemble bulk liquid, and comparison is made of its dielectric constant with that of liquid at the same temperature. If molecular parameters are sought, assumption of the Clausius-Mosotti field or of the Onsager or Kirkwood formulas is necessary.

B. Additivity of Dielectric Constants of Phases upon a Volume-Fraction Basis

The relation

$$\varepsilon = \Sigma \varepsilon_i \delta_i \tag{2-8}$$

where ε_i and δ_i are the dielectric constant and volume fraction of the ith phase, has been used from the earliest investigations, for example, those by Higuti (*8*) and Argue and Maass (*9*). Its use assumes that the dielectric phases run continuously from one plate of the capacitor to the other. Physically this is not the situation, and theoretical justification of the formula is not possible.

C. Procedures with Some Theoretical Basis

The two procedures which seem best on the basis of derived results are the extension of Böttcher's method as developed by McIntosh and his associates (*10, 7*), and the empirical formula due to Fiat and co-workers (*11*). In the first method the several constituents are regarded as forming distinct phases, and Böttcher's method of evaluating the average fields within the phases is adopted. The average polarizability of a phase may then be ascertained, and from this the dielectric constant. With further assumptions the molecular parameters may be calculated if desired.

Fiat et al. (*11*) employ an expression for polarization of each constituent in terms of the dielectric constant of the constituent which is based upon Onsager's distinction between the total internal field at the molecule and the directing field. They attempt to justify the formula by stating that the degree of subdivision of the solids of large surface area usually studied is such as to permit application of formulas valid for homogeneous solutions. The method is therefore discussed in Section 2-4, although it will be shown in that section that the development is empirical.

It may be remarked here that all methods of computing the adsorbate properties contain arbitrary assumptions or empirical statements. A comprehensive discussion of several methods will suffice to illustrate this remark.

D. Extension of Böttcher's Powder Method

In Section 2-2A, where Böttcher's method of dealing with powdered solids was outlined, the essential assumptions were stated explicitly. To extend the development to adsorbate-adsorbent systems requires the assumption that the average field within the solid phase does not alter with adsorbate concentration in the composite system.

The equations now are:

$$E(\varepsilon + 2)/3 = E_1 \delta_1 + E_2 \delta_2 + E_3 \delta_3 \qquad (2\text{-}9)$$

$$E(\varepsilon - 1)/4\pi = C_1 \delta_1 E_1 + C_2 \delta_2 E_2 + C_3 \delta_3 E_3 \qquad (2\text{-}10)$$

where the subscripts 1, 2, 3 refer to the solid, adsorbate, and gaseous matter, respectively. The term $E_1 \delta_1$ is evaluated from the initial condition of no adsorbed matter through the equation $\delta_1 E_1 = (\varepsilon_0 - 1)E/4\pi C_1$, since δ_2 and C_3 are zero. The gaseous phase is considered to occupy spherical interstices, whence $E_3 = [3\varepsilon(\varepsilon_3 + 2)/(2\varepsilon + \varepsilon_3)3]E$. The term $3\varepsilon/(2\varepsilon + \varepsilon_3)$ arises because of the macroscopic field of the spherical inserts of dielectric constant ε_3 surrounded by matter of dielectric constant ε. The second term is due to Böttcher's demonstration that the average internal field within a phase is given by the Clausius-Mossotti term $(\varepsilon + 2)/3$ times the macroscopic field. This expression conforms with the definition of the average polarizability

$$C_i = (\varepsilon_i - 1)3/(\varepsilon_i + 2)4\pi \qquad (2\text{-}11)$$

since $C_3 = (\varepsilon_3 - 1)3/(\varepsilon_3 + 2)4\pi$.

It can then be shown that

$$C_2 \delta_2 E_2 = [(\varepsilon - \varepsilon_0)/4\pi - 3\varepsilon(\varepsilon_3 - 1)\delta_3/4\pi(2\varepsilon + \varepsilon_3)]E \qquad (2\text{-}12)$$

and that

$$(\varepsilon + 2)/3 - \varepsilon(\varepsilon_3 + 2)\delta_3/(2\varepsilon + \varepsilon_3) = (\varepsilon_0 - 1)/4\pi C_1$$

$$+ [\varepsilon - \varepsilon_0 - 3\varepsilon(\varepsilon_3 - 1)\delta_3/(2\varepsilon + \varepsilon_3)]/4\pi C_2 \qquad (2\text{-}13)$$

A plot of the left-hand side of this expression versus $\varepsilon - \varepsilon_0 - 3\varepsilon(\varepsilon_3 - 1)\delta_3/(2\varepsilon + \varepsilon_3)$ yields the quantity C_2, which from the definition yields ε_2. To obtain useful information from this value requires an assumption of the state of the adsorbed matter as well as its dielectric constant in the bulk state. The assumption concerning the state of the adsorbed matter is also required to ascertain the value of δ_2. For many situations in which porous solids are being examined ε_3 may be taken as unity.

E. Extension of Böttcher's Powder Method for Lossy Dielectrics

Essentially the same derivation may be carried through if the composite dielectric shows appreciable loss. McCowan and McIntosh (12) assumed the condition $\varepsilon_3 = 1$, but that both the solid and the adsorbate might exhibit loss. This means that ε, C_1, and C_2 must be treated as complex. Two equations are then obtained,

$$(\varepsilon' + 2)/3 - 3\delta_3\{(2\varepsilon'^2 + \varepsilon' + 2\varepsilon''^2)/[(2\varepsilon' + 1)^2 + (2\varepsilon'')^2]\}$$
$$= (\varepsilon_0' C_1' - C_1' + \varepsilon_0'' C_1'')/4\pi(C_1'^2 + C_1''^2)$$
$$+ [(\varepsilon' - \varepsilon_0')C_2' + (\varepsilon'' - \varepsilon_0'')C_2'']/4\pi(C_2'^2 + C_2''^2) \tag{2-14}$$

and

$$-\varepsilon''/3 + 3\delta_3\varepsilon''/[(2\varepsilon' + 1)^2 + (2\varepsilon'')^2]$$
$$= [C_1''(\varepsilon_0' - 1) - C_1'\varepsilon_0'']/4\pi(C_1'^2 + C_1''^2)$$
$$+ [(\varepsilon' - \varepsilon_0')C_2'' + (\varepsilon_0'' - \varepsilon'')C_2']/4\pi(C_2'^2 + C_2''^2) \tag{2-15}$$

We rewrite these equations as

$$L_1 = A_1 + [(\varepsilon' - \varepsilon_0')C_2' + (\varepsilon'' - \varepsilon_0'')C_2'']/4\pi(C_2'^2 + C_2''^2) \tag{2-16}$$

and

$$L_2 = A_2 + [(\varepsilon' - \varepsilon_0')C_2'' + (\varepsilon_0'' - \varepsilon'')C_2']/4\pi(C_2'^2 + C_2''^2) \tag{2-17}$$

L_1 and L_2 contain only experimentally determinate quantities, since they represent the left-hand sides of the previous equations. A_1 and A_2 are the first terms of the right-hand sides of those equations and contain the quantities C_1' and C_1'' as well as experimentally known quantities. These factors may be evaluated, however, from a knowledge of the initial dielectric constant through the equation

$$(\varepsilon_0 - 1)/4\pi C_1 = (2\varepsilon_0^2 + 5\varepsilon_0 + 2 - 9\delta_3\varepsilon_0)/(6\varepsilon_0 + 3) \tag{2-18}$$

where ε_0 and C_1 are both complex quantities.
The relation

$$(L_1 - A_1)/(L_2 - A_2)$$
$$= [C_2'(\varepsilon' - \varepsilon_0') + C_2''(\varepsilon'' - \varepsilon_0'')]/[C_2''(\varepsilon' - \varepsilon_0') + C_2'(\varepsilon_0'' - \varepsilon'')] \tag{2-19}$$

permits the evaluation of C_2'' in terms of C_2' through the equation

$$C_2^n = [(\varepsilon_0'' - \varepsilon'')(L_1 - A_1) - (\varepsilon' - \varepsilon_0')(L_2 - A_2)]C_2'/$$
$$[(\varepsilon'' - \varepsilon_0'')(L_2 - A_2) - (\varepsilon' - \varepsilon_0')(L_1 - A_1)] = XC_2' \tag{2-20}$$

Thus

$$L_1 = A_1 + [\varepsilon' - \varepsilon_0' + (\varepsilon'' - \varepsilon_0'')X]/[4\pi C_2'(1 + X^2)] \tag{2-21}$$

A plot of L_1 against the coefficient of $1/4\pi C_2'$ for a series of dielectric measurements for different quantities adsorbed yields C_2' and thus C_2''. From the definition of polarizability constant it follows that

$$(\varepsilon_2' - 1)/4\pi = (C_2'\varepsilon_2' - C_2''\varepsilon_2'' + 2C_2')/3 \tag{2-22}$$

and

$$\varepsilon_2''/4\pi = (C_2''\varepsilon_2' - C_2'\varepsilon_2'' + 2C_2'')/3 \tag{2-23}$$

Hence ε_2' and ε_2'' may be evaluated.

2-4 SOLUTION PROCEDURES

A. Solution Method of Channen and McIntosh

Channen and McIntosh (7) assumed that the high specific surfaces of the solids permit the composite dielectric to be regarded as a solution. Böttcher's formulas (13)

$$E(\varepsilon + 2)/3 = \Sigma\delta_k E_{i_k} + (1 - \Sigma\delta_k)E_{i_{\text{cavity}}} \qquad (2\text{-}24)$$

and $\qquad E(\varepsilon - 1)/4\pi = \Sigma\delta_k P_k$

are then employed in conjunction with a molecular-polarizability constant. A molecular polarizability is required since E_{i_k} refers to the local internal field at the kth type of molecule. The polarizability constant γ_k is defined by the equation

$$\tfrac{4}{3}\pi N_k a_k^3 \gamma_k E_{i_k} = N_k(\alpha_k E_{i_k} + \mu^2 E_{r_k}/3kT) \qquad (2\text{-}25)$$

where a_k is the radius of the kth type of molecule and E_{r_k} is the directing field at the kth type of molecule.

E_{i_k} and E_{r_k} are related by the equation

$$E_{i_k} = [1 + (\mu_k^2/3kT)f_k/(1 - f_k\alpha_k)]E_{r_k} \qquad (2\text{-}26)$$

If the field in the solid is assumed independent of the amount of adsorbate and if it can be evaluated by reference to the initial value of the dielectric constant as in the extended Böttcher treatment, it can be shown for the type of system already discussed that

$$(\varepsilon - \varepsilon_0)/4\pi\gamma_2 = (\varepsilon + 2)/3 - 3\varepsilon/(2\varepsilon + 1)$$
$$\times (\delta_4 + \tfrac{4}{3}\pi a_3^3 N_3\{[1 + f_3\,\mu_3^2/(1 - f_3\,\alpha_3)3kT]/(1 - f_3\,\alpha_3)\})$$
$$- (\varepsilon_0 - 1)/4\pi\gamma_1 + 4\pi N_3\,3\varepsilon\{\alpha_3[1 + f_3\,\mu_3^2/(1 - f_3\,\alpha_3)3kT]$$
$$+ \mu_3^2/3kT\}/(1 - f_3\,\alpha_3)(2\varepsilon + 1)4\pi\gamma_2 \qquad (2\text{-}27)$$

where δ_4 designates the volume fraction of free space. Also

$$f_k = (2\varepsilon - 2)/(2\varepsilon + 1)\alpha_k^3 \qquad (2\text{-}28)$$

Thus a plot of

$$(\varepsilon + 2)/3 - 3\varepsilon(\delta_4 + \tfrac{4}{3}\pi a_3^3 N_3\{[1 + f_3\,\mu_3^2/$$
$$(1 - f_3\alpha_3)3kT]/(1 - f_3\,\alpha_3)\})/(2\varepsilon + 1)$$

versus

$$\varepsilon - \varepsilon_0 - 4\pi N_3\,3\varepsilon\{\alpha_3[1 + f_3\,\mu_3^2/(1 - f_3\,\alpha_3)3kT] + \mu_3^2/3kT\}/$$
$$(1 - f_3\,\alpha_3)(2\varepsilon + 1)$$

should yield a straight line of slope $1/4\pi\gamma_2$. Values of α_k may be taken from refractive-index data.

Finally, the relation between dipole moment and γ_2 is

$$\mu^2/3kT = [1 - \alpha_2(2\varepsilon - 2)/a_2^3(2\varepsilon + 1)](4\pi a_2^3\gamma_2/3 - \alpha_2)/$$

$$[1 - 4\pi\gamma_2(2\varepsilon - 2)/3(2\varepsilon + 1)] \quad (2\text{-}29)$$

Although this treatment is in some respects formally similar to the extended Böttcher development, it should be emphasized that the field E_{i_k} is a local field and γ_k a molecular property. In the extended Böttcher procedure the field is an average field within a phase and C_2 is a volume-average polarizability. It is this latter fact which permits ε_2 to be deduced from a knowledge of C_2, and the molecular parameters associated with ε_2 must be calculated by assuming Onsager's equation (14).

B. Solution Method of Fiat, Folman, and Garbatski

Fiat, Folman, and Garbatski (11) have recognized the inadequacy of Debye's formula, which does not distinguish the total internal field and that part of it which acts to direct a dipolar molecule. This situation is very clearly discussed by Böttcher (13), and as a result of Onsager's ideas, the polarization of a homogeneous solution is expressed by $P = (\varepsilon - 1)(2\varepsilon + 1)/9\varepsilon$ where ε is the dielectric constant of the solution.

Fiat, Folman, and Garbatski accept this expression for polarization and assume the additivity of polarizations of each species on a volume-fraction basis. They argue that a porous adsorbent such as porous glass in plate form is inhomogeneous only on the molecular scale as the fine pores have diameters of 15 to 10 A. They then write, using the additivity rule,

$$P = (\varepsilon_1 - 1)(2\varepsilon_1 + 1)\delta_1/9\varepsilon_1 + (\varepsilon_2 - 1)(2\varepsilon_2 + 1)\delta_2/9\varepsilon_2$$

$$+ (\varepsilon_3 - 1)(2\varepsilon_3 + 1)\delta_3/9\varepsilon_3 \quad (2\text{-}30)$$

where ε_1, δ_1 are for the solid, and so on, as in Section 2-3D. With this expression the value of the dielectric constant of glass is readily given, since $\delta_2 = 0$ and $\varepsilon_3 = 1$. In the case of porous glass exact agreement was found with the value given in the literature, namely, 3.75. On neglect of the gas-phase polarization

$$P_2 \delta_2 = (\varepsilon - 1)(2\varepsilon + 1)/9\varepsilon - (\varepsilon_1 - 1)(2\varepsilon_1 + 1)\delta_1/9\varepsilon_1 \qquad (2\text{-}31)$$

and the molar polarization from the formula

$$P_{2_m} = P_2 \delta_2 M_2 V/W_2 \qquad (2\text{-}32)$$

where M_2 is the formula weight of the adsorbate, W_2 the amount adsorbed, and V the volume of porous adsorbent. No assumption is required concerning the density of the adsorbate.

It should be observed in connection with this development that the polarization of each component is expressed through the value of its macroscopic dielectric constant. This immediately implies that the estimate of the internal field and hence the directing field acting upon each species may be assessed through the dielectric constant of that species, i.e., that a molecule of component one is surrounded by, and forms part of, a continuum of material of dielectric constant ε_1. Particularly if a dispersion of components on the molecular scale is assumed as the model, each molecule must be considered surrounded by a medium (solution) of dielectric constant ε. The equation is therefore not consistent with a degree of subdivision such as that used to rationalize the use of a formula applicable to solutions. Nevertheless, since it has been stressed earlier that no completely satisfactory procedure for calculation has been developed, this formula must also be judged in the light of the reasonableness of the dielectric parameters which it predicts. Further discussion will be reserved until experimental results have been recorded.

C. The Differential Specific Polarization

Kurosaki (*15*) has used a procedure in dealing with adsorbed water in silica gel which starts with the assumption of the

Onsager-Kirkwood formula,

$$(\varepsilon - 1)(2\varepsilon + 1)/9\varepsilon\rho = p_k \tag{2-33}$$

where p_k is the specific polarization. On adding an amount of water δW to the composite dielectric, both ε and ρ are altered. Thus

$$\delta p_k = \frac{1}{\rho}\frac{\partial}{\partial\varepsilon}\left(\frac{(\varepsilon - 1)(2\varepsilon + 1)}{9\varepsilon}\right)\frac{\partial\varepsilon}{\partial W}\delta W$$
$$+ \left(\frac{(\varepsilon - 1)(2\varepsilon + 1)}{9\varepsilon}\right)\frac{\partial}{\partial\rho}\left(\frac{1}{\rho}\right)\frac{\partial\rho}{\partial W}\delta W \tag{2-34}$$

The differential specific polarization of water is given by

$$\frac{\partial p_k}{\partial W} = \frac{(2\varepsilon^2 + 1)(\partial\varepsilon/\partial W)}{9\varepsilon^2\rho} \tag{2-35}$$

since the second term of (2-34) was shown to be negligible in comparison with the first. Further reference is made to Kurosaki's results in Section 5-2.

REFERENCES

1. C. J. F. Böttcher, "Theory of Electric Polarisation," pp. 415ff., Elsevier, Amsterdam, 1952.
2. O. Wiener, *Abhandl. Math.-Phys. Kl. Sächs Akad. Wiss. (Leipzig)*, **32**, 509 (1912).
3. D. A. G. Bruggeman, *Ann. Physik*, **5**, 636 (1935).
4. C. J. F. Böttcher, *Rec. Trav. Chim.*, **64**, 47 (1945).
5. K. Kamiyoshi, *Sci. Rept. Res. Inst. Tohoku Univ.*, **1**, 305 (1949).
6. S. Ono, T. Kuge, and N. Koizumi, *Bull. Chem. Soc. Japan*, **31**, 34 (1958)
7. E. W. Channen and R. McIntosh, *Can. J. Chem.*, **33**, 172 (1955).
8. I. Higuti, *Bull. Inst. Phys. Chem. Research Tokyo*, **20**, 489 (1941).
9. G. H. Argue and O. Maass, *Can. J. Research*, **B13**, 156 (1935).
10. R. McIntosh, E. K. Rideal, and J. A. Snelgrove, *Proc. Roy. Soc. (London)*, **A208**, 292 (1951).

11. D. Fiat, M. Folman, and U. Garbatski, *Proc. Roy. Soc. (London)*, **A260**, 409 (1961).
12. J. D. McCowan and R. McIntosh, *Can. J. Chem.*, **39**, 425 (1961).
13. C. J. F. Böttcher, " Theory of Electric Polarisation," pp. 174ff., Elsevier, Amsterdam, 1952.
14. L. Onsager, *J. Am. Chem. Soc.*, **58**, 1486 (1936).
15. S. Kurosaki, *J. Phys. Chem.*, **58**, 320 (1954).

CHAPTER 3

VARIATIONS OF ε' AND ε''

WITH FREQUENCY AND TEMPERATURE

3-1 INTRODUCTION

Böttcher (1) and Fröhlich (2) have shown that the general form of Debye's equations relating ε' and ε'' to the frequency of the measuring field follows from an exponential approach to the equilibrium value of polarization. Fröhlich in particular shows this in a very general way, which will be outlined. The relaxation time τ relating polarization and time is a function of temperature, and the explicit form of the dependence upon temperature is governed by the physical system as represented by the model. There are several models which obey the Debye relations and which might be considered to relate to adsorbed films. A very different situation which leads to the phenomenon of resonance absorption should also be considered relevant in view of the representation of an adsorbate molecule as a rotational oscillator given by Kurbatov and others. Finally, since the transition from an ordered assembly of dipoles in solids to a disordered assembly may be followed by means of dielectric measurements, some discussion of this phenomenon will be given, based again upon Fröhlich's development. It will be seen that variations of ε' or ε" with temperature differ significantly for these situations and help may be expected in rationalizing the behavior of adsorbed molecules.

3-2 THE DEBYE EQUATIONS

On the basis of the superposition principle and $D = \varepsilon E$ one may write the dielectric displacement

$$D(t) = \varepsilon_\infty E(t) + \int_{-\infty}^{t} E(u)\alpha(t - u)\,du \qquad (3\text{-}1)$$

where α expresses the decay of polarization with time for a dielectric in a periodic field $E(t)$.

On differentiation with respect to time there is obtained

$$\frac{d}{dt}D(t) = \varepsilon_\infty \frac{d}{dt}E(t) + \int_{-\infty}^{t} \frac{d}{dt}\left[E(u)\alpha(t - u)\,du\right] + E(t)\alpha(0) \qquad (3\text{-}2)$$

Since $\alpha(t)$ is proportional to $e^{-t/\tau}$,

$$\frac{d}{dt}\alpha(t) = \left(\frac{-1}{\tau}\right)\alpha(t)$$

and $$\tau \frac{d}{dt}D(t) = \tau\varepsilon_\infty \frac{d}{dt}E(t) - \int_{-\infty}^{t} E(u)\alpha(t - u)\,du + \tau E(t)\alpha(0)$$

$$(3\text{-}3)$$

Adding this to the original equation gives

$$\tau \left[\frac{d}{dt} D(t) - \varepsilon_\infty E(t) \right] + D(t) - \varepsilon_\infty E(t) = \tau E(t)\alpha(0) \quad (3\text{-}4)$$

$\alpha(0)$ is determined by considering the case of equilibrium in a constant field so that

$$\frac{d}{dt} [D(t) - \varepsilon_\infty E(t)] = 0 \quad \text{and} \quad D(t) = \varepsilon_s E$$

whence

$$\alpha(0) = (\varepsilon_s - \varepsilon_\infty)e^{-t/\tau}/\tau$$

The differential equation is thus

$$\tau \frac{d}{dt} (D - \varepsilon_\infty E) + D - \varepsilon_\infty E = \tau(\varepsilon_s - \varepsilon_\infty)E \quad (3\text{-}5)$$

Upon employing for a periodic field $E = E_0\, e^{j\omega t}$ and introducing the complex dielectric constant $\varepsilon = \varepsilon' - j\varepsilon'' = \varepsilon(\omega)$, the differential equation yields

$$\varepsilon(\omega) - \varepsilon_\infty = (\varepsilon_s - \varepsilon_\infty)/(1 + j\omega\tau) \quad (3\text{-}6)$$

which on rationalization gives

$$\varepsilon' - \varepsilon_\infty = (\varepsilon_s - \varepsilon_\infty)/(1 + \omega^2\tau^2) \quad (3\text{-}7)$$

and

$$\varepsilon'' = (\varepsilon_s - \varepsilon_\infty)\omega\tau/(1 + \omega^2\tau^2) \quad (3\text{-}8)$$

The dependence of ε' and ε'' on frequency is given explicitly, but the dependence on temperature arises through the variations of $\varepsilon_s - \varepsilon_\infty$ and τ with that variable.

The shape of these curves of ε' and ε'' as a function of frequency is well known and is given for reference in Figure 3-1. For constant temperature the maximum of ε'' occurs at some frequency $\omega_m = 1/\tau$. Hence τ may be ascertained at any temperature. Also the validity of the equations may be tested by noting that at the frequency of the maximum

$$\varepsilon' = (\varepsilon_s + \varepsilon_\infty)/2 \quad \text{and} \quad \varepsilon'' = (\varepsilon_s - \varepsilon_\infty)/2 \quad (3\text{-}9)$$

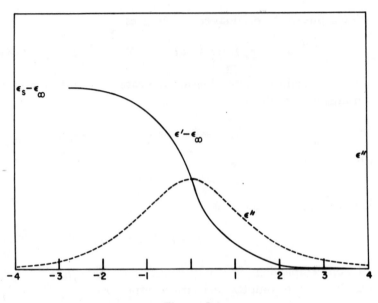

Figure 3-1

The real and imaginary parts of the complex dielectric constant as a function
of frequency for a system obeying the Debye relations.

Because of the difficulty of establishing a sufficiently broad
range of frequency, temperature is commonly varied at constant
frequency or for a range of frequencies insufficient to define the
maximum. This is a less direct means of testing the validity
of the Debye equations, but it may be employed in the following
manner:

Since

$$\varepsilon''/(\varepsilon_s - \varepsilon_\infty) = \omega\tau/(1 + \omega^2\tau^2) \qquad (3\text{-}8)$$

if $\varepsilon_s - \varepsilon_\infty$ and ε'' are known, the function $\varepsilon''/(\varepsilon_s - \varepsilon_\infty)$ may be
plotted against temperature. For fixed frequency the maximum
of the plot will be given by

$$\frac{d}{dT}[\omega\tau/(1 + \omega^2\tau^2)] = 0 = \frac{d}{d\tau}[\omega\tau/(1 + \omega^2\tau^2)](d\tau/dT) \qquad (3\text{-}10)$$

so that τ at the temperature of the maximum equals $1/\omega$. To test the Debye equations, the relation

$$\omega^2\tau^2 = (\varepsilon_s - \varepsilon')/(\varepsilon' - \dot{\varepsilon}_\infty) \tag{3-11}$$

is recalled. With these terms known at T for the maximum, ε'' at that temperature is given by

$$\varepsilon'' = (\varepsilon_s - \varepsilon')^{\frac{1}{2}}(\varepsilon' - \varepsilon_\infty)^{\frac{1}{2}} \tag{3-12}$$

The disadvantage of this procedure is that, in the cases where the Debye equations are expected to hold, $\varepsilon_s - \varepsilon'$ and $\varepsilon' - \varepsilon_\infty$ are small.

It should be noted in connection with the relaxation time used above, that it is a constant arising from a macroscopic measurement. In the models which are to be discussed τ is used to designate a microscopic constant. These two are not the same, since the appropriate expressions for the internal field should be employed in relating the macroscopic observation to the behavior of individual molecules. If the Onsager (3) internal field is employed, the factor relating microscopic to macroscopic relaxation time is $3\varepsilon_s/(2\varepsilon_s + \varepsilon_\infty)$ so that the maximum discrepancy varies between 1 and $\frac{3}{2}$. As the factor relating the two relaxation times involves the dielectric constants ε_s and ε_∞, it is not dependent upon frequency but it will depend upon temperature. However, as an exponential variation of relaxation time with temperature arises from another cause in the models discussed by Fröhlich, no distinction will be made between the microscopic and macroscopic relaxation times.

3-3 MODELS WHICH LEAD TO THE DEBYE EQUATIONS

A. Relation to Relaxation Times

Models which will result in the Debye equations may lead to an explicit expression for τ in terms of parameters which permit the variation of τ with temperature to be predicted. The simplest of these involves a charged particle which has two equilibrium positions separated by some distance b and which requires an activation energy H to surmount the potential-energy barrier between the two positions. The particle oscillates with a frequency $\omega_0/2\pi$ around either of these equilibrium positions. On application of a field the energy levels of the equilibrium positions are altered slightly with respect to the height of the barrier, and the transition probabilities in the two directions are thus also altered. Fröhlich's analysis of this case (4) leads to the expressions $\tau = \pi e^{H/kT}/\omega_0$, where H is the height of the potential barrier, which is much greater than kT. The law of exponential approach to equilibrium, namely,

$$N_2 - N_1 = N e \mathbf{f} \cdot \mathbf{b} (1 - e^{-2\omega_{21}t})/2kT \qquad (3\text{-}13)$$

where N_2 and N_1 are the numbers in the two positions and ω_{21} is the transition probability of a particle going from position 2 to position 1 per second, identifies the transition probability ω_{21} with $1/2\tau$. This model leads to the exponential-decay function and hence the Debye equations only when the particles may be considered as independent of one another. Otherwise transition probabilities for a particle are not constant but depend upon the positions of neighbors.

B. Dipolar Solids

Fröhlich (5) assumes a model for dipolar solids in which the molecules, because of the crystalline field, have, in the simplest case, two equilibrium positions with opposite dipole directions. At low temperatures, because of interaction between dipoles, an ordered arrangement exists. At a temperature T_0 an order-disorder transition occurs, and for $T > T_0$ long-distance order disappears. Order relative to neighbors persists until very much higher temperatures. At the high temperatures the Debye equations hold and also at temperatures appreciably below T_0.

In the high-temperature region and in the absence of a field, the lowest energy level of a dipole is the same in both directions. It is considered that an energy of at least H is required for the molecule to turn from one equilibrium position to the other. The transition probability to turn from position 1 to position 2 with no applied field

$$\omega_{12} = 1/2\tau = \omega_a e^{-H/kT}/\pi A \qquad (3\text{-}14)$$

where π/ω_a is the average time required for an excited molecule to turn from one position to the other and $1/A$ is a factor varying only slowly with temperature and which is required because of internal excitation of the molecule. In a field $\mathbf{f}$, the potential energy required for the two positions is then $H \pm \boldsymbol{\mu} \cdot \mathbf{f}$, and the transition probabilities are then

$$\omega_{12} = \omega_a e^{-(H-\mu f)/kT}/\pi A \simeq (1 + \boldsymbol{\mu} \cdot \mathbf{f}/kT)/2\tau$$

and $\qquad\qquad\qquad \omega_{21} = (1/2\tau)(1 - \boldsymbol{\mu} \cdot \mathbf{f}/kT) \qquad (3\text{-}15)$

The equations

$$\frac{dN_1}{dt} = -N_1\omega_{12} + N_2\omega_{21}$$

$$\frac{dN_2}{dt} = -N_2\omega_{21} + N_1\omega_{12} \qquad (3\text{-}16)$$

and $N = N_1 + N_2$ expresses the rates of change of numbers of dipoles in the respective orientations and the relationship to the total number of molecules. The net change is given by

$$\frac{d}{dt}(N_2 - N_1) = -(\omega_{12} + \omega_{21})(N_2 - N_1) + (\omega_{12} - \omega_{21})N$$

$$= -(1/\tau)(N_2 - N_1) + (\mu f/\tau kT)N \qquad (3\text{-}17)$$

Solving these equations, we find the solution

$$N_2 - N_1 = N\mu f(1 - e^{-t/\tau})/kT \qquad (3\text{-}18)$$

and this yields an exponential approach to equilibrium for

constant field with relaxation time τ. It is to be noted that

$$\tau = \pi A e^{H/kT}/2\omega_a \qquad (3\text{-}14)$$

so that a variation of τ with temperature is predicted. The factor A is identified as being approximately D_0/D_H, where D_0 is the number of energy levels in a range kT near the ground state and D_H is the number in a range kT near the excited state above H. The factor ω_a is usually assumed to be of the order 10^{12} to 10^{14} per sec, so that examination of τ as a function of temperature by the standard way of plotting $\ln \tau$ against $1/T$ will identify H and the intercept at $1/T = 0$ may be checked as to order of magnitude on the basis of the values of ω_a and A.

At low temperatures an ordered arrangement of the dipoles is expected, and the energy of the dipole should depend upon its own direction, since its neighbors may be assumed to be in their ground states. The exponential approach to equilibrium may again be proved (5), and thus the Debye relations will hold. In the intermediate region of temperature near T_0, where the order-disorder transition occurs, dipoles do not behave independently and the Debye relations do not hold. In terms of the static dielectric constant ε_s one would expect a low value in the low-temperature region, which increases quite rapidly near T_0. Above T_0 the value should diminish with temperature in the same way as occurs in polar gases or liquids. The Debye equations should be obeyed at low temperatures and at high, provided that dipole interaction is absent, which would be the case in dilute systems.

C. Dipolar Liquids

The behavior of dipolar liquids was analyzed originally by Debye (5a), and the analysis led to the formula $\tau = 4\pi a^3 \eta/kT$ for the relaxation time of the rotation in a viscous medium. This is a microscopic relaxation time. Here a is the radius of the assumed spherical molecule and η, the coefficient of viscosity of the medium. If this formula were applicable, the variation of τ with temperature should be essentially that of the change of η with temperature. The viscosity coefficient of liquids is known to vary proportionately to $e^{H\eta/kT}$ so that $\tau \propto e^{H\eta/kT}$. Fröhlich (6) has emphasized, however, that the development would be valid only if dipoles do not interact and the relation would apply to such systems as dilute solutions of dipolar molecules in nonpolar solvents when the viscosity coefficient is that for the solvent. For an adsorbate the concept of rotation within a viscous medium is likely to be useful only for molecules in multilayers or in the adsorbate which has condensed into the larger capillaries of a porous adsorbent by the capillary-condensation mechanism. In either case the adsorbate has formed a liquidlike structure of dipolar molecules, and interaction between dipoles must occur. Thus theories such as Onsager's, which are more closely applicable to pure dipolar fluids, might appear to be required in any discussion of such films. On the other hand, Smyth (7) quotes work of Dalbert, Magat, and Surdut on methyl alcohol and on ethyl alcohol, for which substances the predicted types of Debye curves are closely followed by the experimental values in the range 1 cm to 10 m for the wavelength of the applied field. Smyth (8) states, on the basis of calculated molecular radii obtained from the equation $\tau = 4\pi a^3 \eta/kT$ compared with radii from viscosity of gases or from liquid-state densities, that the equation does not adequately represent the relation among relaxation time, viscosity, and molecular radius. However, the ratio of τ/η, as in the case of propyl alcohol, is sometimes nearly proportional to the reciprocal of temperature (8). On this basis, but on the understanding that an approximation is being made, adsorbate in pores and in multilayers should be examined to see whether or not the temperature coefficient of τ is predicted by the temperature coefficient of η.

It has been shown by Powles (3) as mentioned in Section 3-2

that the use of a complex dielectric constant in developing the Onsager equation leads to a relation between ε' and ε'' which is not found experimentally. To make the microscopic relaxation time conform with the experimentally observed behavior, Powles has shown that the relating internal field factor between microscopic and macroscopic relaxation times must be $3\varepsilon_s/(2\varepsilon_s + \varepsilon_\infty)$ and thus varies between unity and $\frac{3}{2}$. On this basis neglect of temperature variations in this factor seems legitimate in comparison with the exponential term, and this practice is reinforced because of the uncertainty in the procedures for obtaining the appropriate value of the constant ε_2'' of the adsorbate. It seems sufficient, therefore, to obtain the relaxation time of the adsorbate from the values of ε_2'' at different frequencies and to compare this, which is a variation of a macroscopic τ, with the variation of the microscopic relaxation time involved in the viscosity coefficient η.

3-4 DISTRIBUTION OF RELAXATION TIMES

When conformity with the Debye equations is not found by use of the tests discussed above or some other device such as the Cole-Cole semicircular plot (9), the usual explanation is based upon a number of relaxation times rather than a single one as assumed in the preceding developments. Fröhlich (10) again provides an illuminating treatment along the following lines.

It is supposed, because of the distinct environment of each individual dipole, that instead of a single potential-energy barrier H there are many such characteristic barriers depending upon the individual dipole. If the polarizing field is removed, the contribution to the polarization of the dipoles having a narrow range of energy near H will decay exponentially with a relaxation time τ, as has already been shown. The relaxation time, rather than the energy H, may be used to classify the dipoles. If $y(\tau)\,d\tau$ is the contribution to the static dielectric constants from the molecules having relaxation times within the range $d\tau$, and if the contributions of the various groups are additive because there is no interaction among them,

$$\varepsilon_s - \varepsilon_\infty = \int_0^\infty y(\tau)\,d\tau \qquad (3\text{-}19)$$

where $y(\tau)$ is the distribution function of relaxation times. The dipoles with a relaxation time in the range $d\tau$ make a contribution to the decay function $\alpha(t)$, which is proportional to $e^{-t/\tau}$, and to $y(\tau)\,d\tau/\tau$, which corresponds to the coefficient of the exponential term in the equation $\alpha(t) = (\varepsilon_s - \varepsilon_\infty)e^{-t/\tau}/\tau$ derived earlier by considering the case of a constant field. The total contribution of all dipoles is thus

$$\alpha(t) = \int_0^\infty e^{-t/\tau}y(\tau)\,d\tau/\tau \qquad (3\text{-}20)$$

The general equation for the complex dielectric constant $\varepsilon' - j\varepsilon''$ by using the principle of superposition and the relations

$$\varepsilon' - \varepsilon_\infty = \int_0^\infty \alpha(x)\cos\omega x\,dx \qquad \text{and} \qquad \varepsilon'' = \int_0^\infty \alpha(x)\sin\omega x\,dx$$

$$(3\text{-}21)$$

may be written $\varepsilon - \varepsilon_\infty = \int_0^\infty \alpha(x)e^{-j\omega x}\,dx$. In the present case this becomes

$$\varepsilon - \varepsilon_\infty = \int_0^\infty \left(\int_0^\infty e^{-x/\tau}y(\tau)\,d\tau/\tau \right) e^{-j\omega x}\,dx$$

$$= \int_0^\infty y(\tau)\,d\tau/\tau \int_0^\infty e^{-j\omega x - x/\tau}\,dx = \int_0^\infty y(\tau)\,d\tau/(1 + j\omega\tau)$$

$$(3\text{-}22)$$

Separating this into its real and imaginary parts leads to

$$\varepsilon' - \varepsilon_\infty = \int_0^\infty y(\tau)\,d\tau/(1 + \omega^2\tau^2)$$

and

$$\varepsilon'' = \int_0^\infty \omega\tau y(\tau)\,d\tau/(1 + \omega^2\tau^2) \qquad (3\text{-}23)$$

Since $y(\tau)$ is always positive, this expression leads to a wider curve of ε'' versus ω, provided only a single maximum is obtained, than for the Debye curves. There will be represented a superposition of a variety of Debye curves of varying τ.

Fröhlich (10) considers a model of two dipole directions of equal energy, but with a different energy barrier H for each dipole, such that $H = H_0 + V$, where $0 \leqslant V \leqslant V_0$. As the contribution to the static dielectric constant does not depend upon the potential-energy barrier, although the individual relaxation time does, according to the equations

$$\tau = \tau_0 e^{V/kT} \tag{3-24}$$

and $\qquad\qquad \tau_0 = \pi A e^{H_0/kT}/2\omega_a \tag{3-25}$

Fröhlich obtains a distribution function

$$y(\tau) = (\varepsilon_s - \varepsilon_\infty)kT/V_0\tau \qquad \text{if } \tau_0 \leqslant \tau \leqslant \tau_1 = \tau_0 e^{V_0/kT} \tag{3-26}$$

and $\quad y(\tau) = 0 \qquad\qquad\qquad \text{if } \tau < \tau_0 \text{ and } \tau > \tau_1 \tag{3-27}$

This distribution function corresponds to an equal distribution of potential barriers over a range V_0 and depends upon temperature. Its relative width

$$(\tau_1 - \tau_0)/\tau_0 = e^{V_0/kT} - 1 \tag{3-28}$$

decreases with increasing temperature. The maximum value of ε'' diminishes with increase of V_0. Details of the discussion may be found in Fröhlich's text.

From our standpoint the possibility of a range of potential-energy barriers and hence of relaxation times is of importance. In Chapter 1 it was pointed out that adsorbing surfaces are known to be energetically heterogeneous. One would therefore expect a variety of relaxation times and departures from the simple Debye relations. However, in the present state of our knowledge the detailed examination of distribution functions is of less consequence than making certain that the increased width of the loss curve relative to the Debye curve is indeed caused by this factor. It is quite possible that other causes may lead to broad loss curves, as has been suggested, for example, by Chapman and McIntosh (*11*), and the most important first objective is to distinguish freely rotating molecules or those undertaking jumps between two equilibrium positions and molecules which, because of oscillations, are showing resonance absorption. Because of this Fröhlich's treatment of resonance absorption for a damped oscillator is fully described in the following paragraphs.

3-5 RESONANCE ABSORPTION

In the case of charged species which oscillate about some equilibrium position with a natural frequency $\omega_0/2\pi$, damped oscillations about the equilibrium polarization are to be expected. Fröhlich assumes a decay function

$$\alpha(t) = \gamma e^{-t/\tau} \cos(\omega_0 t + \psi) \qquad (3\text{-}29)$$

where the constants γ and ψ must be determined. This expression may be substituted immediately in

$$\varepsilon - \varepsilon_\infty = \int_0^\infty \alpha(x) e^{-j\omega x}\, dx$$

to yield

$$\gamma \int_0^\infty e^{-x/\tau - j\omega x} \cos(\omega_0 x + \psi)\, dx = \tfrac{1}{2}\gamma\tau \cos\psi \{(1 + j\tan\psi)/$$

$$[1 - j(\omega_0 - \omega)\tau] + (1 - j\tan\psi)/[1 + j(\omega_0 + \omega)\tau]\} \quad (3\text{-}30)$$

The two constants γ and ψ are evaluated by considering the cases of very low and very high frequencies. For $\omega \ll \omega_0$, ε'' is small, and $\varepsilon' = \varepsilon_\infty + \Delta\varepsilon$, where $\Delta\varepsilon$ is real. Neglecting ω in comparison with ω_0,

$$\Delta\varepsilon = \gamma\tau(\cos\psi - \omega_0\tau\sin\psi)/(1 + \omega_0^2\tau^2) \qquad (3\text{-}31)$$

For very high frequencies at which $\omega \gg \omega_0$, the influence of the restoring force which causes oscillation is considered negligible during one period of the field. Behavior such as that predicted by the Debye theory should obtain. Then, since $\Delta\varepsilon = \varepsilon_s - \varepsilon_\infty$, one may write

$$\varepsilon - \varepsilon_\infty = \Delta\varepsilon/(1 + j\omega\tau) \qquad \text{for } \omega \gg \omega_0 \qquad (3\text{-}32)$$

so that on combining this expression with

$$\varepsilon - \varepsilon_\infty = \gamma\tau \cos\psi/(1 + j\omega\tau) \qquad (3\text{-}33)$$

then

$$\Delta\varepsilon = \gamma\tau \cos\psi \qquad (3\text{-}34)$$

It then follows from the low-frequency expression for $\Delta\varepsilon$ that

$$\tan\psi = -\omega_0\tau \qquad (3\text{-}35)$$

Insertion of this value in (3-30) yields

$$\varepsilon' - \varepsilon_\infty = \tfrac{1}{2}\Delta\varepsilon \{[1 + \omega_0(\omega + \omega_0)\tau^2]/[1 + (\omega + \omega_0)^2\tau^2]$$
$$+ [1 - \omega_0(\omega - \omega_0)\tau^2]/[1 + (\omega - \omega_0)^2\tau^2]\} \qquad (3\text{-}36)$$

and

$$\varepsilon'' = \tfrac{1}{2}\Delta\varepsilon \{\omega\tau/[1 + (\omega + \omega_0)^2\tau^2] + \omega\tau/[1 + (\omega - \omega_0)^2\tau^2]\}$$
$$(3\text{-}37)$$

The important feature of this development is that power loss may be examined in detail. At constant temperature ε'' will be a maximum when

$$\omega_m = (1 + \omega_0^2\tau^2)^{1/2}/\tau \qquad (3\text{-}38)$$

This relation is readily obtained after making the substitutions $(\omega + \omega_0)\tau = a$ and $(\omega - \omega_0)\tau = b$, since either of the conditions $\partial\varepsilon''/\partial a = 0$ or $\partial\varepsilon''/\partial b = 0$ leads to the desired result. The maximum value of

$$\varepsilon'' = \tfrac{1}{2}\Delta\varepsilon (1 + \omega_0^2\tau^2)^{1/2} \qquad (3\text{-}39)$$

The relaxation time τ as usual must be considered as dependent upon temperature and to decrease with increasing temperature. At high temperatures and hence with $\omega_0\tau \ll 1$, $\omega_m \simeq 1/\tau$, and $\varepsilon'' \simeq \tfrac{1}{2}\Delta\varepsilon$ at the frequency of the maximum.

At low temperatures with $\omega_0 \tau \gg 1$, $\omega_m \simeq \omega_0$, and $\varepsilon'' \simeq \frac{1}{2} \Delta\varepsilon \, \omega_0 \tau$, again at the frequency of the maximum. Comparison of the Debye type of absorption and resonance absorption in terms of $2\varepsilon''_{max}/\Delta\varepsilon$ shows for the Debye situation $2\varepsilon''_{max}/\Delta\varepsilon = 1$, independent of temperature, while for resonance absorption $2\varepsilon''_{max}/\Delta\varepsilon = \omega_0 \tau$ at low temperatures and 1 at high. This means that, if ω_0 does not vary markedly with temperature, then the ratio $2\varepsilon''_{max}/\Delta\varepsilon$ should narrow and become high at low temperatures. The comparison is made in Figure 3-2, which is essentially Fröhlich's figure 17. Further, since $\omega_m(T) = 1/\tau(T)$ for the Debye case, the frequency of maximum absorption diminishes with increasing τ

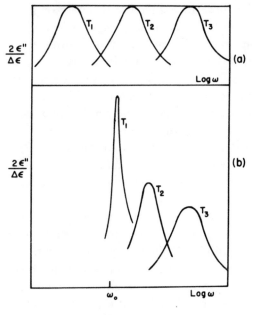

Figure 3-2

Debye type of loss and resonance loss as a function of frequency at several temperatures. The Debye type of loss is illustrated in the upper part of the figure (a), resonance loss in the lower (b).

without limit, whereas the frequency of maximum loss of the resonating system tends to the limit ω_0 with increasing relaxation time.

The behavior in respect of losses is thus widely different in the two cases. Given experimental data for a sufficient range of conditions, the distinction between an oscillatory dipole and one exhibiting Debye behavior should be possible for adsorbates. One difficulty which may be anticipated is the fact that, in addition to the complication from the heterogeneity of the surface, adsorbed molecules may be located in the first molecular layer or in higher layers. Thus, in the general case, if first-layer molecules are oscillators due to the strong field of force from the surface, while those in higher layers rotate or jump from one equilibrium position to another, composite loss curves consisting of both types may be found. Low quantities adsorbed, using solids on which the gases adsorb with a large heat of adsorption, should restrict the matter under examination very closely to first-layer molecules. An indication of conditions is readily given by reference to the Brunauer-Emmett-Teller (B-E-T) equation, from which the fraction held in the first layer may readily be calculated by the equations $\theta = (V/V_m)(1 - p/p^0)$ and $V_1 = V_m \theta$, where θ is the fraction of the surface covered, V_1 the amount in the first layer, and V_m the amount required to complete the monolayer (12).

Adsorbates held in solids with wide pores and near conditions of saturation are known to have properties not greatly different from those of liquid and may, as already mentioned, resemble the Debye type of liquids. Films at low temperatures, if composed largely of multilayers, might be expected to show the behavior of dipolar solids. However, many pieces of evidence, for example, work by Litvan and McIntosh (13) and Patrick and Land (14), support the view that the transition to solid films occurs many degrees below the normal triple point of the substance. The transition temperature is in some cases a sensitive function of the amount adsorbed, in others almost independent of that factor, as shown by Hodgson and McIntosh (*15*). Generally, the greater the amount adsorbed in porous media, the closer to the bulk transition temperature is that of the adsorbed matter. However, transition in an adsorbed phase is not sharp and occurs over a range of temperature. Thus a clear-cut distinction between the oscillatory and the Debye type of absorption may be difficult, but the importance of that distinction is clear.

REFERENCES

1. C. J. F. Böttcher, "Theory of Electric Polarisation," pp. 345ff., Elsevier, Amsterdam, 1952.
2. H. Fröhlich, "Theory of Dielectrics: Dielectric Constant and Dielectric Loss," pp. 7ff., Clarendon Press, Oxford, 1949.
3. J. G. Powles, *J. Chem. Phys.*, **21**, 633 (1953).
4. H. Fröhlich, "Theory of Dielectrics: Dielectric Constant and Dielectric Loss," pp. 66ff., Clarendon Press, Oxford, 1949.
5. H. Fröhlich, "Theory of Dielectrics: Dielectric Constant and Dielectric Loss," pp. 79ff., Clarendon Press, Oxford, 1949.
5a. P. Debye, "Polar Molecules," Chemical Catalog Company, Inc., New York, 1929, pp. 77ff.
6. H. Fröhlich, "Theory of Dielectrics: Dielectric Constant and Dielectric Loss," p. 89, Clarendon Press, Oxford, 1949.
7. C. P. Smyth, "Dielectric Behavior and Structure," p. 105, McGraw-Hill, New York, 1955.
8. C. P. Smyth, "Dielectric Behavior and Structure," p. 103, McGraw-Hill, New York, 1955.
9. K. S. Cole and R. H. Cole, *J. Chem. Phys.*, **9**, 341 (1941).
10. H. Fröhlich, "Theory of Dielectrics: Dielectric Constant and Dielectric Loss," pp. 91ff., Clarendon Press, Oxford, 1949.
11. I. Chapman and R. McIntosh, *Can. J. Chem.*, **40**, 92 (1962).
12. T. L. Hill, *J. Chem. Phys.*, **14**, 268 (1946).
13. G. Litvan and R. McIntosh, *Can. J. Chem.*, **41**, 3095 (1963).
14. W. A. Patrick and W. E. Land, *J. Phys. Chem.*, **38**, 1201 (1934).
15. C. Hodgson and R. McIntosh, *Can. J. Chem.*, **38**, 958 (1960).

CHAPTER 4

EXPERIMENTAL

4-1 INTRODUCTION

The usual apparatus employed in examining the gas-solid systems consists of three distinct parts. The first is the evacuation and gas-measuring section, the second is the dielectric cell and its thermostat, and the third is the electrical device used for measuring the real and imaginary parts of the complex dielectric constant. The first of these is usually a volumetric means of measuring the amount of gas adsorbed and a device to obtain the equilibrium pressure over the adsorbate. These assemblies have been described many times (*1, 2*), and details of their design and construction need not be restated. To a large degree the same comment may be made concerning the electrical arrangements, although in one or two cases recently improved experimental techniques require some discussion. The design of cells and thermostats warrants brief comment also.

4-2 ELECTRICAL MEASUREMENTS

A. Required Precision of Measurement and Appropriate Circuits in the Frequency Range 500 cps to 100 Mcps

Precision, or sensitivity, of measurement is of relatively more consequence than absolute accuracy, although the latter must not be neglected, for absolute values of the properties of the adsorbate must be known within the limits which permit comparison with data available for bulk matter. For example, an absolute error of 5 per cent, say, in the dielectric constant of an adsorbate does not prohibit the recognition of the adsorbed state as one in which the molecules rotate in similar fashion to those in bulk liquid. On the other hand, except in the use of porous adsorbents, and even with these under conditions not approaching saturation of the solid, the amount of gaseous matter in the solid-adsorbate system is very small. Porous adsorbents may take up more than 30 per cent by weight at high equilibrium pressures, but for an amount of water, for example, corresponding to 20 per cent of the first molecular layer, only 0.06 g/g of adsorbent is involved for a solid of specific surface 1,000 m^2/g. Nonporous solids of specific surface as much as 50 m^2/g are difficult to obtain and with water as the adsorbate would take up only about 0.02 g/g at the completion of the unimolecular layer. Reference to the various formulas used in calculating the adsorbate's properties shows that the initial value of dielectric constant for solid without adsorbate is usually subtracted and changes from that value represent the contribution of the adsorbed matter. In a particular case which may be used as illustration, the initial dielectric constant without adsorbate was 1.863 and after saturation with butane was 1.935. Hence sensitivity of the electrical apparatus to changes of capacity of the test cell is mandatory for many systems.

In the frequency range from about 500 cps to several hundred kilocycles it is satisfactory to use carefully constructed bridges such as the Schering bridge (3). From the latter frequency to about 10 Mcps the use of a resonance circuit with sensitive and stable vacuum-tube voltmeter detector is convenient. Even in this range, as Rosen (4) has recently commented, care must be exercised in correcting for the effect of lead inductances, and the length of these leads may govern the type of cell and its position relative to the electrical measuring devices. Inductive ratio arm bridges have been used in this range of frequency and to somewhat higher values (4). Within the range of 1 to 100 Mcps a resonance system may be used provided that the test cell itself can be adjusted to bring the circuit to resonance, for in these circumstances lead corrections cancel. The principles to be followed are given by Hartshorn and Ward (5), who first clearly demonstrated both the theory and practice of the use of a resonant circuit at high frequencies. An adaptation to solid-adsorbate systems was employed successfully by Waldman and McIntosh (6) and by Channen (7) (see Figure 4-3). Beyond this frequency, methods involving the study of standing waves are required. Coaxial lines may be used to frequencies of 4,000 Mcps, and hollow waveguides and resonant cavities have been used with signals of 3- and 1-cm wavelengths. A recent improvement in the experimental technique for coaxial lines and an analytical procedure for solving the basic equation in standing-wave systems are worthy of discussion. The development of the latter is deferred to Appendix A.

B. Improved Precision in the Voltage–Standing-Wave Ratio

In examining the standing-wave system of a coaxial line, the inverse voltage–standing-wave ratio (VSWR), which is the ratio of the amplitude of the wave at a minimum to its amplitude at a maximum, and the distance of the first minimum from the dielectric surface at the end of the line are the necessary experimental quantities.

Alternatively, examination of the shape of the wave near the minimum will yield the same information of the ratio of amplitude at the minimum to that at the maximum. In either case precision of measurement of the amplitude of the minimum is important, and, regardless of the sensitivity of the detection device, fluctuations of the amplitude of the standing wave may obscure the result. In the author's experience, attempts to stabilize the input voltage of the Klystron generators were not effective. To overcome the difficulty, part of the signal from the generator was taken from another line or a magic tee, rectified, and fed through a voltage divider. The signal from the detector of the standing-wave line was compared with the signal in the voltage divider, by use of photoelectric or direct-current (d-c) amplifier and galvanometer (8). Signal fluctuations thus compensated one another, and the desired data could be obtained with errors of 0.1 per cent or less. This degree of accuracy was lost if the standard charts available in Von Hippel's book (9) were employed, so that the analysis given in Appendix A was developed by Shigeishi (10).

4-3 CELLS

A. Cells Suitable to L-F Measurements

A typical cell for use with powders and for low-measuring frequencies is represented in Figure 4-1. It consists of three coaxial cylinders, of which the central cylinder is insulated from

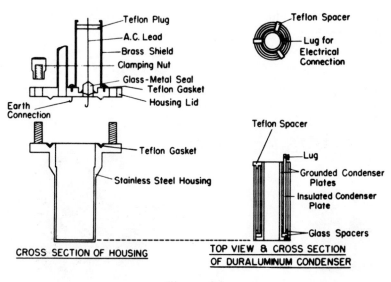

Figure 4-1

A coaxial cell suitable for powders and measuring frequencies up to several megacycles per second.

the other two, which are connected to the grounded cell housing. Separation of the cylinders is such that a capacity of 10 to 15 $\mu\mu f$/cm is obtained for vacuum between the plates. The separation of about 0.08 cm is sufficient to permit many fine particles to lie between the plates. Use of metals of low coefficient of expansion such as Invar, and of glass or Teflon spacers, provides a cell with small temperature coefficient of capacity. A metal of low coefficient of expansion is required if tubes of adsorbents such as porous glass are made to give a sliding fit with the metal cylinders. If gaps between sample and electrodes are permitted, a correction for this fact must be made, as was done by Fiat and co-workers (*11*) by assuming that the space and dielectric form two capacitors in series.

A cell employed in the study of hydrogen chloride adsorbed

upon sodium chloride of specific surface about $40 \, m^2/g$ is shown in Figure 4-2. The use of many plates to increase the

Figure 4-2

A multiplate cell employed with finely divided sodium chloride as the adsorbent.

capacitance is well illustrated. During the filling of either of these cells vibration of the cell is necessary to ensure uniform packing and reasonable density of the powder bed. In the case of a powder such as sodium chloride, which sinters at room temperature in the presence of water vapor, the filling must be carried out with cell and powder in a dry box.

Cells of this type may be used in metal or glass containers until frequencies of about 10 Mcps are reached. At this stage of the frequency range other designs are necessary, for the corrections for lead inductance become very large. As indicated in the section dealing with the electrical circuits, the design of cells for higher frequencies up to 100 Mcps must be such as to permit retuning of the resonant circuit by adjustment of the test cell itself. A suitable type of cell is illustrated in Figure 4-3

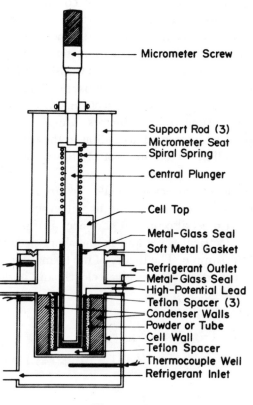

Figure 4-3

A dielectric cell suitable for use from several megacycles per second to several hundred megacycles per second. Inductance corrections are avoided by following the procedure suggested by Hartshorn and Ward.

and incorporates the features of design recommended by Hartshorn and Ward (5).

B. Coaxial Lines

If a coaxial-line system is used with a cell of fixed position for the short-circuiting plate, thin-walled German silver tubing may be successfully employed in the construction of the cell because of its good electrical properties. As is frequently the case, the region of the line containing the sample may be held at temperatures very different from room temperature. The thin tubing is advantageous, for it reduces transfer of heat along the tube. In designing such lines, care must be taken to see that no electrical junction reflects the electromagnetic wave. Where different dimensions of conductors are necessary, tapered connections must be formed according to the recommendations given by Purcell in "Techniques of Microwave Measurements" (12).

The sample of dielectric should be ground or otherwise shaped so that it makes a sliding fit with the inner and outer conductors. It must also present end faces at right angles to the path of the electrical wave and to the short-circuiting plate at the end of the sample. The theory of the formation of the standing wave in the coaxial line is given clearly and in detail in Von Hippel's books (9, 13).

The requisite equations are

$$\tanh \gamma_2 d / \gamma_2 d = (-j\lambda_1/2\pi d)(E_{min}/E_{max}$$
$$- j \tan 2\pi x_0/\lambda_1)/[1 - j(E_{min}/E_{max}) \tan 2\pi x_0/\lambda_1]$$

$$(4\text{-}1)$$

and $\qquad \varepsilon' = -KT^2 \cos 2\tau$

$$\varepsilon'' = KT^2 \sin 2\tau$$

$$(4\text{-}2)$$

In these, γ_2 is the complex propagation factor of the wave in medium 2, d is the thickness of the sample, x_0 its distance from the first minimum of the standing wave, and λ_1 the wavelength in the air part of the guide. The term $\gamma_2 d$ may be expressed as $Te^{j\tau}$, and once the values of T and τ are known, the values of ε' and ε'' follow from (4-2) (see Appendix A).

C. Resonant Cavities

In some cases, as described by Folman (14) and Feldman et al. (15) very valuable information concerning the adsorbed state has been obtained by studying the loss or imaginary part of the complex dielectric constant at high frequencies with waveguides or resonant cavities used. A brief description of the techniques is given, but it should be remembered that the relationship between ε'' and ε' must be known before a complete dielectric description can be given; alternatively some relation must be assumed between ε'' and μ before the apparent dipole moment μ of the adsorbate can be evaluated.

Waveguides are employed in the same manner as coaxial lines, i.e., the standing wave is examined by means of a traveling probe, and the VSWR and distance of the minimum from the dielectric are ascertained. Equations (4-1) and (4-2) are again used to obtain ε' and ε''.

The particular advantage of cavity resonators is that energy is not lost by radiation as in open-line systems, and very high values of Q, which is proportional to the ratio of the phase factor to the attenuation factor β/α, may be achieved. Low-loss dielectrics may be studied with precision because of this, but lossier materials with greater difficulty because the resonance curve becomes asymmetric. Two closely related procedures may be employed to obtain $1/Q = \tan \delta$. The energy sustaining the wave in the guide varies with $Y'(O)^2$, the input admittance, and falls to half value when the cavity is detuned from resonance by a change in phase Δ, of $\pm (\alpha/\beta)n\pi$, since

$$Y'(O)^2 = 1/(Z_1')[\Delta^2 + (\alpha n\pi/\beta)^2] \qquad (4\text{-}3)$$

where Z_1' is the characteristic impedance of medium one (*13*). The detuning results from changing the length of the cavity from its resonance length by

$$\pm \Delta X_h / 2 = \pm \alpha l / \beta \qquad (4\text{-}4)$$

or by changing the input frequency from its resonance value

$$\nu_0 \text{ to } \nu_0 \pm \Delta \nu_h / 2 \qquad \Delta \nu_h / 2 = \pm (\alpha / \beta) \nu_0$$

Since

$$\Delta X_h / l = 2\alpha / \beta = \Delta \nu_h / \nu_0$$

the relative half width between half power points is the same on either scale. Since losses by walls or other dielectrics (a gaseous atmosphere, for example) add directly, $1/Q = \sum 1/Q_i$, where Q_i is the factor for the appropriate dielectric. To obtain ε' and ε'', the distance X_0 of the first minimum from the boundary of the dielectric is required. Then, as Von Hippel shows (*13*) for a cavity resonator $E_{\min}/E_{\max} = \alpha l = 2\alpha \beta l / 2\beta$, where l is the length of the cavity. But $\beta = 2\pi/\lambda$, and $Q = 2\beta/\alpha$, hence $E_{\min}/E_{\max} = \pi l / Q \lambda$. Equation (4-1) may now be used, with $\pi l / Q \lambda$ in place of $E_{\min}/E_{\max}$. However, the Q employed must be that due to the dielectric alone, not that of dielectric and walls of the cavity together.

Waveguide assemblies have been used by Folman and his associates (*14, 15*), employing wavelengths of about 3 cm and 1 cm. A representation of two of the assemblies is given in Figure 4-4. One cavity could be tuned and was designed for measurements at room temperature.

D. Cell Housings

The container for a cell designed for low frequencies may conveniently be made of glass or of metal. Where glass is employed, it is preferable to avoid designs which incorporate greased joints. Metal jackets are convenient but require gaskets which will withstand extremes of temperature and still

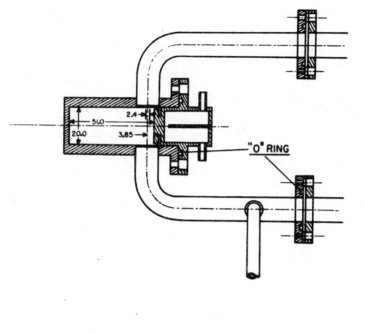

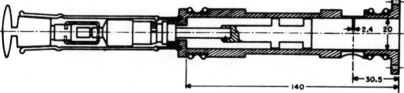

Dimensions in mm

Figure 4-4

A fixed cavity and a tunable cavity both used at a frequency of 23.500 Mcps. The fixed cavity could be heated to 300°C, and its lower temperature limit was − 78° C. The tunable cavity was employed at room temperature.

provide vacuum-tight assemblies which may be pumped to pressures of 10^{-6} mm Hg. Teflon gaskets, used with tongue-and-groove sealing designs, are satisfactory to about −80°C.

They may be unsatisfactory at temperatures approaching the normal boiling point of liquid nitrogen. Gaskets made of soft annealed gold have been used successfully between -190 and $+200°C$, and the temperature of evacuation may be increased by cooling the part of the assembly near the gasket (*16*). Indium gaskets are also satisfactory.

The passage of electrical leads through the cell housing may be arranged by using button-type glass-metal seals soldered into position or a double arrangement of Kovar-glass seals. Hard solder is preferable. Thermocouple leads may be inserted through Conax glands, but experience with this type of seal has been only moderately satisfactory. It has been found preferable to introduce the thermocouple leads through the glass line for pumping or gas admission at some point remote from the cell housing and thus at room temperature. De Khotinsky cement then provides a leak-free wax seal.

4-4 CONTROL OF TEMPERATURE

Thermostats which may be employed throughout a very wide range of temperature and which permit little variation of temperature are now regarded as standard laboratory devices. To provide environments from $-180°C$ to room temperature and maintain the dielectric cells free from temperature gradients requires care, however, and the arrangements depend to some extent upon the form of the dielectric cell. Since the provision of low temperatures is necessary to create conditions in which losses may be observed at moderate frequencies in adsorbates which are simple molecules, a type of assembly which has been found suitable will now be described.

The arrangement consists of a large Dewar flask about 12 in. in diameter containing liquid nitrogen. The level of the refrigerant is maintained within narrow limits by means of an electronic switch and a valve to the supply of liquid nitrogen.

The circuit has been described by Fred and Rauh (*17*). The actuating thermal elements are carbon resistances with negative temperature coefficients of resistance. By moving the height of the resistances within the Dewar, the level of the liquid may be varied. Inside the Dewar is a stainless-steel jacket, with a diameter 3 to 4 in. greater than that of the cell housing. The space between cell housing and jacket may be evacuated or may contain helium when heat transfer across the gap between jacket and cell is desired.

The cell housing is attached to the lid of the steel jacket by a thin-walled (0.001-in.) stainless-steel tube to provide support and to restrict thermal conduction from the top. Attached to the central supporting tube is a system of metal vanes. The central tube to which the vanes are attached is wound with a heating element. The cell's container is also wound with a heating element over that part of it which contains the dielectric cell. Thermocouple junctions are attached beneath the cell heating element at top and bottom of the cell section, so that temperature gradients may be detected and eliminated. With helium between cell container and jacket, the temperature drops during several hours to $-180°C$. On adjusting the wattage dissipated in the two heaters, temperatures between -180 and $0°C$ may be achieved without gradients in the cell. For low temperatures helium is left in the jacket; for temperatures above about $-90°C$ it is removed. The level of nitrogen may require adjustment to lower levels at the higher temperatures. In practice gradients of $0.1°C$ are observed, and the consumption of liquid nitrogen is about 1 liter/hr.

4-5 PREPARATION OF THE SURFACE

The preparation of a known and reproducible surface presents many difficulties, which have been overcome in few instances.

As has already been shown, successful investigation is dependent upon a large specific surface. This means the use of very fine powders or of porous adsorbents. The former are difficult to make, and the latter present more complicated situations in the rationalization of data because of the unknown influence of pore structure. Even if the factor of pore structure could be eliminated, many of the gel systems contain firmly bound water or chemisorbed hydroxyl groups. In the case of very fine powders there is the danger of loss of surface due to heating or moisture, or both. In practice, therefore, compromises have had to be accepted, and it must be remembered that some of the experimental facts arise because of heterogeneous surfaces and, in some cases, actual bonding between the adsorbate and some chemical group already attached to the surface.

As might be expected, the attempt to cleanse a surface so that physical adsorption may be studied involves heating and high vacuum. With modern mechanical and diffusion pumps, pressures in the order of 10^{-6} mm Hg, are readily achieved, provided that glassware and stopcock greases are heated or sparked. Elimination of mercury vapor from the adsorption system would appear necessary, although no clear evidence has ever been given that its presence affects results. Elimination of mercury may complicate the design of manometers and the means of admission of known quantities of gas. Neverthless, elimination is recommended. Similarly, greased stopcocks may now be discarded in favor of metal valves. Again, no clear evidence is available to show the influence of stopcock grease, but if the adsorption system is held at low temperatures for extended periods of time, some contamination can be expected. It is a matter of common experience, for example, that samples of porous silica glass become yellow to brown after long exposure in adsorption systems, and the contaminants can be removed only by oxidation and leaching. On the other hand, such contaminated samples have shown no variation in their adsorptive properties to butane or water from the original characteristics of the clean sample, as demonstrated by Quinn (*18*).

In the general case, then, pumping should be carried out with the sample at the highest temperature which can be maintained without destruction of area. In practice a wide range of temperatures has been employed, from about 60 to 700°C. In spite of this, agreement in the general nature of the results has been quite good.

In the case of porous silica glass, special treatments have been developed to eliminate or vary the number of hydroxyl groups attached to the surface. It was shown by Sidorov (*19*) and by Folman and Yates (*20*) that hydroxyl groups remain bonded to the silicon even after heating under vacuum. These are adsorption sites which permit hydrogen bonding, as Yates and co-workers (*21*) have demonstrated. Removal of these groups is achieved by heating in combination with chemical treatment. Perhaps the best procedure is that described by Chapman and Hair (*22*), based upon a patent issued to Elmer, namely, U.S. Patent 2,982,053.

Treatment with a fluoride such as aqueous NH_4F followed by repeated leaching and by heating to high temperature, say, 700°C, under vacuum, replaces the OH groups by fluoride and does not cause collapse of the porous structure. Heating under vacuum alone will reduce the amount of OH with some loss of surface (*14*). The partial removal or the elimination of this group is observed by infrared absorption measurements, which show a band in the region 3,600 to 3,750 cm^{-1}.

Folman (*14*) has exchanged the hydrogen for deuterium so that ND_3 might be studied. Another case where special preparation of the surface has been examined is reported by Thorp (*23*). As will be seen in greater detail later, Thorp (*23*) has reported hysteresis in the dielectric property of gel systems and a marked dependence of values upon frequency in an l-f range.

Some of this has been eliminated by very thorough removal of water-soluble substances, as shown by Nair (*24*).

In summary, then, practice has varied widely in the cleansing of surfaces and in protecting them from recontamination. This fact must be remembered in examining results, although the agreement of general findings has been widespread. More and more care is being taken to establish known surfaces, and this effort should be intensified.

REFERENCES

1. S. Brunauer, "The Adsorption of Gases and Vapors," Vol. I, pp. 32ff., Princeton University Press, Princeton, N.J., 1945.

2. P. H. Emmett, "Advances in Colloid Science," Vol. I, Wiley (Interscience), New York, 1942.

3. L. Hartshorn, "Radio Frequency Measurements by Bridge and Resonance Methods," Chapman, London, 1947.

4. D. Rosen, *Trans. Faraday Soc.*, **59**, 2178 (1963).

5. L. Hartshorn and D. Ward, *J. IEE*, **79**, 597 (1936).

6. M. Waldman and R. McIntosh, *Can. J. Chem.*, **33**, 268 (1955).

7. E. W. Channen, Thesis, University of Toronto, 1950.

8. J. D. McCowan and R. McIntosh, *Can. J. Chem.*, **39**, 425 (1961).

9. A. Von Hippel, "Dielectric Materials and Applications," M.I.T. Press, Cambridge, Mass., and Wiley, New York, 1954.

10. R. Shigeishi, Thesis, Queen's University, Kingston, Ontario, Canada, 1965.

11. D. Fiat, M. Folman, and U. Garbatski, *Proc. Roy. Soc. (London)*, **A260**, 409 (1961).

12. E. M. Purcell, in "Techniques of Microwave Measurements" (C. G. Montgomery, ed.), McGraw-Hill, New York, 1947.

13. A. Von Hippel, "Dielectrics and Waves," Wiley, New York, 1954.

14. M. Folman, Microwave Studies of Adsorbed Molecules, *Technion Rept.*, Israel Institute of Technology, Haifa, Israel, 1962.

15. U. Feldman, C. H. Schonfeld, and M. Folman, *Trans. Faraday Soc.*, **59**, 2394 (1963).

16. G. Litvan and R. McIntosh, *Can. J. Chem.*, **41**, 3095 (1963).

17. M. S. Fred and E. G. Rauh, *Rev. Sci. Instr.*, **21**, 258 (1950).

18. H. W. Quinn, Thesis, University of Toronto, 1956.

19. A. N. Sidorov, *Russian J. Phys. Chem. (English Transl.)*, **30**, 183 (1956).

20. M. Folman and D. J. C. Yates, *Trans. Faraday Soc.*, **54**, 1684 (1958).

21. D. J. C. Yates, N. Sheppard, and C. L. Angell, *J. Chem. Phys.*, **23**, 1980 (1955).

22. I. Chapman and M. L. Hair, *J. Catalysis*, **2**, 145 (1963).

23. J. M. Thorp, *Trans. Faraday Soc.*, **55**, 442 (1959).

24. N. K. Nair, private communication, 1964.

CHAPTER 5

EXPERIMENTAL RESULTS

5-1 INTRODUCTION

Emphasis has been placed in earlier sections on the necessity of employing solids of large specific surface, since this permits easier experimental examination of the systems. Porous adsorbents such as silica gel, titania gel, and porous glass have therefore been used frequently. Other substances such as cellulose which have large adsorptive capacities have also been employed, although less frequently. Nonporous adsorbents of large specific surface are more difficult to obtain and have been

61

infrequently examined. The major portion of experimental results is thus derived from the more complicated systems, and these results will now be considered. Many of the published investigations are touched upon, but no attempt is made to cite all the literature. Rather, the aim is to present the common findings by reference to pertinent papers.

5-2 POROUS ADSORBENTS

A. Results with Titania and Silica Gels

One of the early and extensive investigations is due to Higuti (1), who examined the behavior of n-propyl and isoamyl alcohols adsorbed in titanium oxide gel. A wide range of temperature from −70 to +70°C was employed, as well as a set of frequencies from about 0.4 to 3 Mcps. A representation of his findings is indicated in Figure 5-1. As the general nature of these results is in agreement with other investigations, the facts represented in the figure form a reasonable basis for discussion and comparison.

Although there is some variation with frequency of the increment of capacity per unit amount of adsorbate, it is not great and does not help materially in examining the problem of frequency dependence of properties. However, the variations with quantity adsorbed and with temperature are of major significance. At any temperature and frequency, a linear increase in the capacity of the test cell with quantity adsorbed is found until a critical amount of adsorption has been achieved. A second linear section of increased slope is then observed at all but the highest temperature. For this latter condition the second linear section has a lesser slope than the first, which conforms with findings by Kurbatov (2) and McIntosh et al. (3) for silica gel and as later work shows for porous glass substrates. A third linear section was also reported by Higuti, who

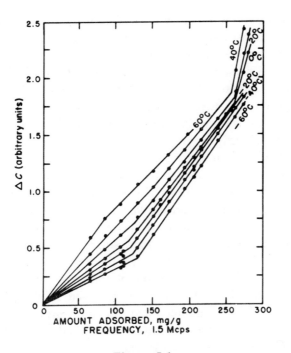

Figure 5-1

Data obtained by Higuti for the *n*-propyl alcohol–titania gel system. Note the three linear sections of progressively increasing slope except at the highest temperature

interpreted these linear regions in the following way. The first section is considered to be due to adsorbed matter in the first layers, where, because of the influence of the surface field, orientational polarization might be expected to be small (see Section 1-2). The second region of higher slope is considered to mark the range of capillary condensation. The capillary adsorbed material resembles bulk liquid in its properties, as various investigations by Amberg, Morrison and Drain, and others have shown (*4, 5, 6, 7, 8*). The orientational polarization should achieve more nearly normal values for such adsorbate, and the increased slope is thereby explained. The third linear section is considered by Higuti to be due to free liquid. The variation of capacitance with quantity and the effect of temperature are greater for this range of amount adsorbed than in the capillary condensed range.

Although it is stated above that frequency had a minor effect on results, Higuti has emphasized that the onset of dispersion occurs at lower temperatures for longer wavelengths and that this observation is similar to the behavior of polar liquids. Thus the capillary condensed adsorbate resembles bulk liquid in its properties, although quantitative agreement is not found.

Quantitative agreement in the dielectric constant is not likely to be found in any event, since Higuti employed the additivity of dielectric constants on the basis of volume fraction of the phase. The unlikelihood of this procedure leading to correct results has already been discussed in Sec. 2-3B. No special treatment was accorded the data when losses were observed, and so the absolute values of dielectric constant need not be recorded. This early investigation remains of consequence, however, since the existence of regions of adsorption of varying dielectric properties is clearly demonstrated, and the general behavior of polar adsorbates in porous adsorbents is revealed.

Higuti's findings were soon confirmed, independently, by McIntosh and colleagues (3) and by Kurbatov (2). The first group employed silica gel as the adsorbent and such adsorbates as ethyl chloride and butane. Frequencies in the l-f range were used, and the volume-fraction addition rule of dielectric constants was again utilized. The approach and results differed in several ways from those of Higuti. First, McIntosh and his associates employed a nonpolar adsorbate, butane, as well as polar adsorbates. The adsorbate being nonpolar, the value of its dielectric constant should not differ greatly from that of butane in a bulk phase of comparable density and should afford a test of the method of calculation. Second, the effect, if any, due to the porous nature of the adsorbent should be revealed without complications arising from an unknown orientational polarization.

These experiments and later ones of improved accuracy from the same laboratory (9, 10) revealed two linear sections of the data when increment of capacity was plotted against quantity adsorbed, and this was the case whether the adsorbate was polar or nonpolar. In contrast with Higuti's findings the slope of the second linear section was always lower than that of the first. Only the result at the highest temperature employed by Higuti is in agreement with this. It is not, however, a matter of consequence, since later investigations reveal that the temperature coefficients of these slopes may differ.

The dielectric constant calculated for butane was found, on the assumption of a liquid-state density of the adsorbate, to be 1.84 along the first section and 1.57 along the second. The value for butane from the refractive index is approximately 1.9 at the same temperature so that the employment of (2-8) seems justifiable for matter adsorbed in the first layer. The anomaly of the lower value of the second section has not been adequately explained, although attempts to account for it have been made (9). However, the support for the use of (2-8) is not substantial, since adsorbates of low dielectric constant are the most likely to lead to correct results by any procedure.

It was found also in the investigation of silica gel that the temperature coefficient of the slopes of the plots was small, even in the case of ethyl chloride, and that the apparent dielectric constant of ethyl chloride was less than 6, in comparison with a value of about 10 for bulk liquid. Kurbatov (2) obtained more definitive data on this point in the study of both acetone and water taken up by a silica gel. His data showed clearly a negligible variation of slope with temperature and gave values of polarization, based on the assumption of the Clausius-Mosotti field, which were such as to reveal an important contribution to the total polarization from the orientational polarization. He made an important advance in explaining this by showing that a dipole which oscillates in three dimensions may contribute an important orientational polarization but will have a negligible variation of that contribution with temperature. His formula was stated in Section 1-2, and a development of the formula for a rigid dipole oscillating in a plane is given in Appendix C.

B. Discontinuities in the Slopes

Speculation as to the cause of the change of slope between the linear sections has been common. Higuti (1) distinguished the position marking the junction of the first two linear sections as indicating the completion of an adsorptive region and the inception of capillary condensation. McIntosh and his associates (3) as well as Kurbatov (2) have examined the situation for possible correlation with V_m, the volume required to complete the unimolecular layer. The former group could find little to support the view that the discontinuity of slope marks the completion of the first layer. Kurbatov (2) does suggest that V_m is marked by the position of the change of slope. Snelgrove et al. (11) established that the position of the change of slope in terms of quantity adsorbed does not shift appreciably with temperature. However, for the adsorbate butane, it is dependent upon the amount of water in the gel. Increased water content shortens the first linear section. In addition the slope of the second linear section was diminished by the additional water.

Distinct viewpoints concerning the significance of the amount adsorbed at this position of discontinuity of slope are likely to persist. The application of the BET (12) theory to porous adsorbents to estimate specific surface is common but is open to such objections as expressed by Pierce and coworkers (13).

It seems that the suggestion that adsorption in capillaries is beginning has merit. Some explanation must be advanced for the reduced slope of the second linear section which is found with silica gels or glass and which is observed for nonpolar as well as polar adsorbates. As will be brought out in detail in Section 7-2, where data for nonporous solids are treated, the completion of the unimolecular layer seems readily distinguishable. Polar molecules in the upper layers usually show increased values of the polarization over those in the first layer. Thus, unless some factor is invoked such as the location of the molecule in a position where it is almost completely surrounded by solid, there seems little reason for an apparently reduced polarization in the case of porous solids. The effect certainly cannot be attributed to restricted rotation in narrow pores, since butane shows the same effect. On the basis of such considerations the beginning of condensation in capillaries appears to offer an acceptable rationalization.

One further factor in these results deserves comment. All investigators are in agreement that the plots are linear. This experimental result shows that the dielectric property of an amount of adsorbate added is independent of the amount already present. On the assumption that experimental precision is sufficient, there appears to be no increasing interaction between adsorbed molecules as the equilibrium population of the surface is increased. Such a finding contradicts the decreasing values of the differential heat of adsorption with quantity adsorbed, which was thoroughly established by Harkins (14). This variation has been attributed to heterogeneity of the surface, repulsive interactions of dipoles and other causes such as the concomitant formation of multilayers. One conclusion only seems possible from the dielectric results. The degree of heterogeneity of the surface fields and the lateral interactions are insufficient in magnitude to be revealed by the electrical measurement of ε'. This conforms with the conclusion reached by Benson, Channen, and McIntosh (*14a*) that large surface-induced dipoles have little effect upon the observed moment. Further work should be conducted to examine this question, as the only publication which clearly reveals an important variation of apparent polarization with adsorption is due to Folman in the case of ammonia on porous glass (*15*), which is reviewed in Section 5-4.

Investigations which have been conducted since these early studies have utilized improved techniques and preferable procedures for calculating the polarization of the adsorbate. These will now be summarized, but it will be seen that they have not established a greatly improved understanding of the phenomenon.

5-3 POROUS SILICA GEL—POROUS GLASS

Similar data to those discussed above for silica gel have been obtained by Petrie (*16*), Chapman(*10*), and McCowan and McIntosh (*17*) using improved techniques and higher frequencies as well as wider temperature ranges. In these cases the calculation of the dielectric properties was performed by employing the extended Böttcher treatment described in Sections 2-3D and 2-3E. Characteristic values are summarized in Tables 5-1 and 5-2. In general it will be seen that the nonpolar adsorbate butane yields the expected value of its dielectric constant for the first linear section of the primary data, but too low a value for the second linear section. Virtually no temperature coefficient is evident, as is to be expected for a nonpolar adsorbate. Ethyl chloride, methyl chloride, and other polar adsorbates show values of dielectric constant less than those for the liquid state. Temperature effects are negligible or within experimental precision for data of the second linear section in all cases.

TABLE 5-1

Typical Data for Adsorbates on Porous Glass

Adsorbate	Temp., °C	First linear section	Second linear section	Refractive index squared	Dielectric constant of liquid from data of Crozier
Butane*	5.0	1.89	1.60	1.81	—
	−6.2	1.85	1.52	1.83	—
	−19.0	1.88	1.55	1.84	—
Ethyl chloride	14.4	8.65	4.53	—	9.2
	−11.3	7.68	4.45	—	11.4
†	11.2	10.2–8.9	5.7	—	9.9
‡	−17.9	10.1–8.1	5.7	—	11.9
	−32.9	9.8–7.2	5.7	—	13.1
	−68.0	6.94	—	—	16.0
§	−95.2	7.20	—	—	18.8
	−121.1	7.33	—	—	22.3

*Data of Petrie and McIntosh.

†These results were obtained by using frequencies between 500 and 4,000 Mcps. The positive temperature co-efficient arises from decreasing losses, which are appreciable.

‡Data of McCowan and McIntosh.

§Data of Chapman and McIntosh.

TABLE 5-2

Typical Data for Adsorbates on Silica Gel*

Adsorbate	Temp., °C	First linear section	Second linear section	Refractive index squared	Dielectric constant of liquid, from Onsager equation
Butane†	0.1	1.80	1.61	1.81	—
	15.0	1.78	1.58	1.79	—
	30.0	1.74	1.55	1.77	—
Methyl chloride	0.1	9.40	5.05	—	12.0
Ethyl chloride	0.1	8.66	4.36	—	11.2
	15.0	7.89	4.14	—	10.5
	30.0	7.50	3.99	—	9.7
†	−30.0	7.20	4.20	—	12.9
	0.0	6.59	4.08	—	11.2
	30.0	5.85	4.00	—	9.7
Water	−15.0	1.069 (69.2)	64.7 (40.0)	—	94.6§
	−6.0	— (74.2)	54.6 (41.5)	—	90.4§
‡‡	9.0	1.052 (61.0)	44.9 (47.2)	—	84.4 ⎫ ICT
	30.0	— (69.2)	69.1 (61.0)	—	76.4 ⎬ values
	44.0	1.052 (69.2)	49.7 (45.0)	—	70.4 ⎭

*$4\pi C_2/3$ is in excess of 1.0 in the case of water. Values in parentheses refer to numbers obtained by the use of the cluster treatment.

†Data of Petrie and McIntosh.   ‡Data of McIntosh, Rideal, and Snelgrove.   §Estimated for undercooled water.

70

A measurable variation of increasing dielectric constant with decreasing temperature is found for the first section, although it is somewhat smaller than for liquid matter. One exception is adsorbed water. As shown in Table 5-2, $4\pi/3$ times the average polarizability of water, computed by the extended Böttcher procedure, is in excess of 1.0 for the first linear section. It does not vary appreciably with temperature. The polarization, and hence dielectric constant, is lower for the second section and again shows a negligible temperature coefficient.

In making the generalizations of the paragraphs above, the absolute values of the dielectric constant of ethyl chloride have been disregarded. No reason is apparent why the values should vary to the extent shown from one experimental assembly and investigator to another. It seems that the differences must arise because of errors in assigning the free space and other parameters of the dielectric, except in the case of McCowan's measurements, which were performed by using coaxial lines. Despite the discrepancies of the absolute values, the statements made concerning the temperature coefficients are undoubtedly valid for those conditions in which losses are negligible. It may also be accepted that the dielectric constant is less than that for the liquid phase at the same temperature.

Because of the anomalous values of water, and because an explanation of the low values of the data from the second linear section was sought, Petrie and McIntosh (16) applied a modification of the cluster treatment outlined in Section 2-2D. As this procedure was purely empirical and not particularly successful, it will not be discussed in detail. It is mentioned, however, since data obtained by using it are given in Table 5-2 to illustrate the negligible temperature effects with adsorbed water.

Kurosaki (18) investigated the silica gel–water system, using frequencies of 2 kcps to 1 Mcps. The adsorption isotherms were obtained at 25 and 35°C. Dielectric data were accumulated for the combined system at 25°C and analyzed to yield the differential specific polarization as discussed in Section 2-4C. This quantity varied from a value of 1 through a value of about 7.5 to a value of about 23, so that Kurosaki identified three adsorption regions. The specific polarization in the third region is greater than that for liquid water, which has a value of 17.7. Since for this large quantity of adsorbed water there is also a maximum in the loss as a function of frequency at about 10 kcps, Kurosaki gave as one possible explanation the existence of very strongly developed hydrogen bonds in the adsorbate. He also offered the theory of binary aggregates, due to Sillars (19), to rationalize results. This theory contains an empirical factor n which is dependent upon the shape of the water aggregate, and its utility is therefore difficult to assess. No definite conclusions about the nature of the adsorbed water were arrived at by Kurosaki, which is understandable in view of the complex nature of porous silica as an adsorbent and the anomalous dielectric behavior of adsorbed water which has been apparent in all the investigations.

Kamiyoshi and Odake (20) observed an l-f dispersion of adsorbed water on silica gel in the region of 1 kcps and lower. The variation of the frequency of maximum loss with temperature led to an activation energy of 8 kcal/mole. The process was concluded to be an ionic migration along the surface, for adsorbed water had been shown by Freymann and Freymann (21, 22) to be in the liquid state down to low temperatures, as will be seen in Section 5-5. Since the water is not in the solid form, which could explain the low frequency of the loss maximum, a conductive type of loss was concluded to be the reasonable alternative.

5-4 POROUS GLASS

The adsorbent porous glass was studied by McIntosh and his associates with the same adsorbates as they had employed in using silica gel. Among the several reasons for doing so were the ability to obtain the adsorbent in both granular and cylindrical form and the knowledge of the pore volume of the porous glass. Results with this adsorbent were so similar to those already quoted for silica gel that no special reference need be made to them except when low temperatures or high frequencies were employed. The knowledge of pore volume demonstrated that the low dielectric constant of butane along the second linear section could not be accounted for by the low density of the adsorbed film, since it could not have been accommodated in the pores at the required density (16).

Chapman and McIntosh (10) examined methyl chloride, ethyl chloride, and butane adsorbed on porous glass which had been pumped out at 300°C. He used a temperature range from 0 to −180°C and a frequency range from 3 kcps to 4 Mcps. The results obtained for methyl and ethyl chlorides were similar and will be summarized for the latter, as it was more extensively investigated.

Two adsorption regions with constant values of dielectric constant were again observed, and as usual the second region had the lower value of that property. Above a temperature of about −130°C no losses were observed. The ethyl chloride adsorbed in the first region revealed a temperature coefficient of ε_2 about one-sixth of that for normal liquid, while that adsorbed in the second region varied by about one-third as much as liquid. The absolute value of dielectric constant was again low in comparison with liquid, namely, about 6 instead of 12. In general these findings confirm earlier ones.

Below the temperature of −130°C both substrate alone and substrate plus adsorbed ethyl chloride showed pronounced losses. The loss in the glass itself is attributable to hydroxyl groups still bound to the surface. The existence of these has been established by Folman and Yates (23) and Sidorov (24). Partial removal of these groups by treatment with aqueous

NH_4F (*10*) reduced the temperature coefficient. Addition of ethyl chloride in quantities well below the monolayer volume enhanced the losses markedly, so much so that in one instance the capacity of the cell fell below that of the substrate alone. A complex between hydroxyl and ethyl chloride was postulated to account for the result. A similar complex is observed with methyl chloride at a lower temperature, but none is observed with butane, which does not affect the observed losses of the substrate. Data for ethyl chloride are shown in Figure 5-2.

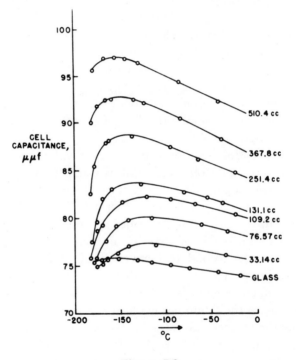

Figure 5-2

Dielectric data for ethyl chloride adsorbed on porous glass. At high temperatures there is no evidence of loss. The crossing of the two lowest curves results in a lower apparent dielectric constant of gel plus adsorbate than gel alone.

TABLE 5-3

(Frequency 50 kcps)

Amount adsorbed cc at NTP	Temp., °C	ε' of composite dielectric	$\varepsilon'' \times 10^2$ of composite dielectric	ε'	ε''	
0.0	−43.0	2.26	2.54	3.30	0.05	⎫
	−95.1	2.29	2.97	3.83	0.06	⎬ Glass
	−131.6	2.31	2.82	3.39	0.05	⎭
33.1	−34.2	2.33	2.12	6.16	0.03	⎫
	−75.7	2.37	2.40	6.78	0.02	
	−110.4	2.39	3.17	7.68	0.03	
76.6	−32.5	2.45	2.26	6.10	0.02	
	−61.0	2.49	2.40	6.89	0.07	
	−116.5	2.52	2.83	7.46	0.06	⎬ Adsorbate
109.2	−68.0	2.59	2.65	6.94	0.03	
	−95.2	2.61	2.83	7.20	0.07	
	−121.1	2.62	2.69	7.33	0.03	
132.1	−79.5	2.65	2.55	7.23	0.04	
	−126.5	2.68	2.98	7.76	0.004	⎭
251.4*	−64.4	2.81	2.41	5.04	0.02	
	−95.5	2.87	2.70	5.52	0.04	
	−137.6	2.92	3.12	6.11	0.02	
361.9	−38.6	2.90	3.27	4.18	0.004	
367.9	−83.1	3.01	2.84	4.71	0.005	
510.4	−124.0	3.08	2.85	5.23	0.004	
	−85.3	3.20	3.13	4.34	0.02	
	−129.6	3.27	2.99	4.72	0.002	

*Second linear region begins at about 150 cc of adsorbate.

Accompanying the losses is the decreasing value of ε_2^1 with increasing frequency. Values of ε_2' and ε_2'' are given in Table 5-3. The values of ε_2' are somewhat greater for the second linear region, owing to the method of calculation, than they would be if a graphical procedure had been employed, but this matter need not be pursued in the present discussion. Broad loss peaks for the adsorbate were obtained, for which the maximum height and the apparent width did not appear to change with temperature over the narrow range of temperature available. Such behavior is characteristic of the Debye type of losses rather than resonance absorption. Since in the temperature region where no loss was observed the temperature coefficient of ε_2' was small, an attempt was made to reconcile the shape of the loss curve with resonance absorption by assuming a very highly damped oscillation.

From the experimental standpoint, the matter adsorbed at very low equilibrium pressures is that which brings about enhanced loss. Interaction with molecules adsorbed at higher surface concentrations is shown by the shifting of the temperature at which loss is observed toward lower values. The same may be said for molecules in the multilayers or condensed in the capillaries. These molecules are apparently not contributors to the loss and diminish the loss of the matter adsorbed in the first layer.

McCowan and McIntosh (17) examined ethyl chloride in porous glass for the temperature range $+11$ to $-22°C$ and the frequency range 500 to 4,000 Mcps, using a coaxial line. Reproducibility at any one frequency was excellent, within ± 0.2 per cent, but became uncertain to ± 2 per cent with variation of frequency. In spite of this McCowan showed that, for quantities of gas corresponding to the first adsorption region, there exists a slight positive temperature coefficient of ε_2' as well as large values of ε_2''. The procedure for calculating these quantities has been given in Section 2-3E. In this investigation

ε_2' was found to correspond quite closely to the value for liquid, as a value of 10.2 was observed at 11°C and 530 Mcps. Liquid, according to the Onsager equation, has a static dielectric constant of 10.5 at 14°C. This differs from results at lower frequencies by more conventional experimental methods, and the cause of the discrepancy is not known. Again, McCowan found that loss was most pronounced in the matter adsorbed at low surface coverages.

Matter in the second adsorption region has the lower apparent dielectric constant, about 6 in value, and has a negligible temperature coefficient of dielectric constant. It thus differs from bulk liquid in this respect. At the highest adsorption and the lowest temperature evidence of slight losses was noted. It is not known whether bulk liquid would exhibit loss or not under these conditions.

5-5 POROUS GLASS AND AMMONIA

A careful study of the porous 96 per cent silica glass and ammonia system was carried out by Fiat et al. (*15*). Emphasis was placed upon the behavior of the ammonia adsorbed in quantities below the amount required for the unimolecular layer. Changes of capacity in the amount of 2×10^{-4} $\mu\mu f$ were observable in a resonance system because of stabilized power supplies and the thermostating of the measuring device in a constant-temperature environment with stability 0.1°C. Amounts adsorbed were measured volumetrically. A correction was applied to the apparent changes of capacity because of the gaps between the porous plate of the adsorbent and the silver electrodes. No test was made, however, for the existence of loss. Evaluation of the polarization of the adsorbate was carried out by the procedure indicated in Section 2-4B. Absolute values of polarization may not be correct, therefore, and this possibility should be borne in mind when values of the differential polarization greater than those for bulk phases are reported. Capacitance varied with time after admission of gas until the equilibrium value was established. It is important to note that capacity increased to a maximum and then diminished to the equilibrium value. Hysteresis was observed in both the plots of capacitance change vs. quantity adsorbed and in the adsorption isotherms.

The two important findings were the nonlinear change of capacitance with quantity adsorbed and the hysteresis. These are illustrated in Figure 5-3, which is Figure 3 of Reference 15.

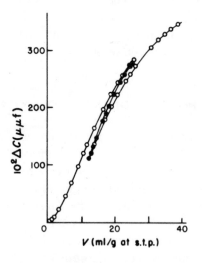

Figure 5-3

Dielectric data for ammonia on porous glass. The data are of high precision and lead to a changing value of polarization with adsorbate content. Filled circles are desorption points.

Based upon such data the differential molar polarization is represented in Figure 5-4, which is Figure 7 of the reference

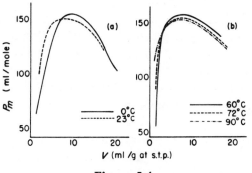

Figure 5-4

The differential molar polarization arising from data such as those in
Figure 5-3.

and which shows the variation of the differential molar polarization with temperature. The explanation of such results offered
by Fiat and co-workers (*15*) is summarized in the succeeding
sections.

The surface of the glass is known to be energetically heterogeneous and consists of different types of adsorption site. The
sites are Si or O atoms or OH groups. These last were considered by Sidorov (*24*) and Folman and Yates (*23*) to be
adsorption sites of polar molecules, and evidence of this was
accumulated by these authors from infrared spectra.

The energy of adsorption for NH_3 is less on these sites. Fiat
et al. thus postulate two types of site, with the energy of
adsorption lower on the OH sites. The time effects are thus
explained, as had also been done by Folman and Yates (*23*).
Adsorption takes place initially on OH sites, and redistribution
to other sites occurs with accompanying reduction of capacity.
On desorption the opposite sequence of events occurs, and OH
sites are liberated first.

The hysteresis is explained on the basis that the contribution to the capacity by molecules on Si and O sites is less than on OH sites, and the fraction of the adsorbed molecules on these more energetic sites is greater on desorption than on the less energetic OH sites, which are the first to become empty. Although these explanations are reasonable, it is implicit in the existence of hysteresis that the adsorption distribution or the desorption distribution or both are not truly equilibrium situations.

Temperature dependence of polarization was normal when the greater quantities of ammonia had been adsorbed; i.e., polarization diminished with increased temperature. The dependence was abnormal for the first amounts of ammonia adsorbed; this was attributed to the firm binding of these molecules to the more energetic sites, which would be the first occupied. With increasing coverage of the surface the differential heat of adsorption is known to diminish, and orientational polarization might be expected to increase.

It is of some interest to note here that Fröhlich (25) has shown that if $d\varepsilon/dT < 0$ for l-f measurements it may be deduced that the application of an external field decreases the entropy of the system, presumably, in such cases, by increasing the order of the system in the direction of the field. Ripley and McIntosh (26) presented an argument to support this conclusion even when losses are observed and the application of classical thermodynamics becomes questionable. Thus, in the ammonia-glass system, the l-f dielectric constant or, had losses been present, the real part of the dielectric constant may be employed to discuss the entropy change upon application of a field. Since $d\varepsilon/dT > 0$ for the material adsorbed at low fractions of the surface coverage, the opposite conclusion must be reached, namely, that the application of the field increases the disorder of the adsorbed matter.

Bearing in mind that the values of polarization calculated by Fiat et al. may be in error because of the formula employed, it is nevertheless of interest to follow their discussion of the results obtained.

Differential molar polarizations for the adsorbed ammonia ranging from 50 to 150 ml^3 were derived. These compare with values of 50 to 103 ml^3 calculated for gas and liquid, respectively, by the Onsager (27) equation. Thus a molar polarization greater than that in the liquid must be accounted for. This is done by assuming that hydrogen bonds formed with the surface OH groups are stronger, as recognized by the shift of the OH stretching vibration, than those in liquid ammonia. The maximum of the differential polarization was accounted for by the saturation of the OH groups. A confirmatory experiment was sought and methylation of the OH groups was employed with the following results. About 80 per cent of the hydroxyl groups were methylated, and the differential polarization rose rapidly to a maximum of about 140 ml^3, just below that found for the unmethylated surface. It then fell very rapidly to a minimum of about 75 ml^3 before beginning to rise slowly as the amount adsorbed increased. The gradual rise was attributed to increasing orientational polarization. The explanation of the results offered was that the first molecules adsorbed attached themselves to the OH groups, and on saturation of these a reduced polarization associated with the other sites was observed.

The authors further consider that the observed moment of 2.42D in comparison with a moment of 1.46D for gaseous ammonia is explicable by the shift of the lone pair of electrons away from the nitrogen to the extent of a 25 per cent shift of its centroid, which is regarded as reasonable by them.

Reference should perhaps be made here to the statements of Section 1-2, where it was concluded that binding to a surface might be expected to cause the adsorbed molecule to act as an oscillator, with consequent reduction of its contribution to orientational polarization and the disappearance of the normal temperature dependence of polarization. If the result reported by Chapman and McIntosh (*10*) for adsorbed ethyl chloride is due to bonding with the hydroxyl groups, it will be seen that an important reduction of polarization occurs in one temperature range and above this range no enhancement of polarization is observed.

Folman (*28*) and Feldman et al. (*29*) have reported microwave studies of adsorbed ammonia on porous glass. Resonant cavities and 1-cm- and 3-cm-wavelength signals were employed. Temperature variation between -78 and $+51°C$ was achieved in certain experiments. Power absorption of adsorbed ammonia was observed and was considered to be of the Debye type. A maximum in tan δ as a function of temperature was observed at 30°C, and the temperature of the maximum was independent of quantity adsorbed. To account for the Debye type of dispersion, the adsorbed dipoles were considered according to Fröhlich's model as discussed in Section 3-3B. The value of the activation energy between the equilibrium positions was deduced to be 2320 cal/mole. When a spectrum of relaxation times was assumed, an activation energy of 4020 cal/mole was calculated as the highest energy barrier between the equilibrium positions (see Section 3-4).

Feldman and colleagues (*29*) attempted also to find the value of the permanent moment of the adsorbed ammonia. They employed the Debye relation among tan δ, μ, concentration, and relaxation time which is applicable to solutions, namely,

$$\tan \delta = (\varepsilon + 2)^2 4\pi\mu^2 cN\omega\tau/\varepsilon 27kT(1 + \omega^2\tau^2) \qquad (5\text{-}1)$$

Relaxation time τ was known from variation of loss with temperature. A permanent moment of 1.2D was deduced and differs substantially from the value 2.4D which resulted from the procedures employed for the l-f data discussed earlier. This is an example of the sensitivity of computed molecular parameters to the methods of analyzing the data for the combined adsorbent-adsorbate systems. In this case the deduced moment of $1.2D$ is lower than that of gaseous ammonia. It would be considered a preferable value by the author, for it is consistent with the view expressed in Section 1-2 that adsorbed molecules should show apparent moments less than exhibited in the gaseous state of aggregation.

A further interesting conclusion of these h-f studies was that adsorbed ammonia cannot undergo an inversion vibration. The conclusion was arrived at by comparing adsorbed NH_3 and adsorbed ND_3. The latter substance was adsorbed upon a glass surface of which the OH groups had been deuterated. The data were identical in the two cases, which would not have been so for gaseous matter unless the inversion vibration had been eliminated.

A private communication from Folman has described the very recent work of Lubezky and colleagues (*30*). These investigators employed three samples of porous glass as the adsorbent for ammonia. A frequency of about 23 kMcps was employed, and a resonant cavity of which the temperature could be varied from -78 to about $85°C$. The three samples of glass, designated R, S, and T, were heated at the temperatures of 450, 850, and $950°C$, respectively, in order to vary the content of OH groups. Sintering occurred at the higher temperatures. Sample S lost area from 122 to 89 m^2/g, for example. The value of ε' of the glass was expected to diminish with reduction of OH content, but the values were 3.47, 2.96, and 3.18, respectively. The value of sample T was considered to result from increased density on sintering.

The major finding was the existence of two loss maxima for sample S when $T \tan \delta$ was plotted against temperature for a fixed quantity adsorbed [see (5-1)]. Such a result had been obtained earlier by Rolland and Bernard (*31*) and by Kamiyoshi and Ripoche (*32*) for the silica gel–water system, as is discussed in Section 5-6. In the present instance, however, the relationship between surface constitution and the existence of the maxima has been developed. By observing the infrared absorption of the three glass samples at 3,730 cm^{-1} or the relative dielectric loss (assumed due to OH groups), an estimate was established of the relative quantities of OH in the three samples. Thus sample R contained five times the amount in sample S, which in turn contained 1.8 times the amount in sample T. The activation energies H for the relaxation process were found to be 1.98 kcal/mole for the low-temperature maximum of sample S and 2.56 kcal/mole for the other maximum. This latter value agreed excellently with the value obtained by using sample T.

These data, in conjunction with the infrared studies of Cant and Little (*33*), led Lubezky, Feldman, and Folman to interpret their data in the following way. Sample R had many OH groups on the surface, and adsorption of ammonia was presumed to occur almost exclusively on these groups for coverage of the surface less than 30 per cent. Sample S had many fewer OH groups, and boron atoms were available in the surface for adsorption. Thus two distinct sets of sites existed in sample S. The lower activation energy for orientation on the OH sites of sample S was rationalized as due to fewer neighboring OH groups to any adsorbed ammonia. Sample T was considered to have very few OH sites, and adsorption occurred predominantly upon the boron atoms. Thus a single type of adsorption site was involved, and consequently a single maximum in the loss as a function of temperature.

Comparison of these statements with those in the first part of Section 5-5 shows that the ideas concerning the nature and relative energies of adsorption sites are changing as information is accumulated. The importance of OH groups on the surface and the evidence of sites of different adsorption characteristics are maintained and reinforced, however.

Shigeishi (*34*) has recently completed a reinvestigation of the porous glass–ethyl chloride system, using frequencies of 1,000 to 4,000 Mcps and a temperature range of -20 to $-191°C$. The porous glass was treated to remove the majority of the OH groups by heating under vacuum to $800°C$. Removal of OH groups was followed by the observation of the infrared absorption spectra for frequencies between 4,000 and 2,300 cm^{-1}. Quantitative evaluation of the extent of removal was not possible, since the original sample permitted no transmission. However, it was clear that reduction of the number of silanol groups was substantial, although not quite complete. Several important results were obtained, and of these the most important discovery was the elimination of the second linear section of the plot of ε' against quantity adsorbed.

At the higher temperatures, i.e., above $-100°C$, and for the entire range of frequencies, the value of ε' increased linearly with quantity adsorbed. The value of the initial slope was thus maintained throughout the range of adsorption and the value of the dielectric constant ε_2' was 6.3. This value is in excellent agreement with values obtained by Chapman and earlier investigators for ethyl chloride along the first linear section. It can thus be said with some assurance that the presence of OH groups is responsible for the second linear section.

Shigeishi has pointed out that three possible explanations for the second linear section of the plots of ε' against amount adsorbed had been offered. These were a sudden change of polarization at a critical quantity adsorbed, a sudden change of density of the adsorbate, and an abrupt alteration of the local field because of a new location of the adsorbate molecules. The first of these appeared unlikely, since butane exhibited the same behavior as polar molecules. The second was proved by Petrie (35) to be impossible, since the required low density of the adsorbate would demand a much larger internal volume to accommodate the matter. The third appeared feasible, since the amount adsorbed at the kink of the plot corresponded approximately with the beginning of the hysteresis loop of the adsorption isotherm. The new observation is not inconsistent with this. The electrical field acting upon the adsorbed matter is apparently modified by the presence of OH groups, and these groups in conjunction with the location of the adsorbate, perhaps in pores, create an environment which reduces the measuring field. This explanation is preferable to the postulate of a complex between ethyl chloride and hydroxyl groups. Chapman and McIntosh (*10*) provided evidence that a complex formed by the observation of a lower value of ε' for glass plus the first admission of adsorbate than for glass alone. Subsequent additions of adsorbate were normal in that the dielectric constant was approximately 6. Shigeishi has confirmed this result for a temperature of $-191°C$ and also has demonstrated that the heat of adsorption is less on the surface which has been largely freed of OH groups. Since with hydroxyl groups present the first quantities of adsorbate are adsorbed more strongly, yet yield the higher value of apparent polarization at the higher temperatures, the molecules forming the complex are not those which may be identified with the lower apparent polarization of the second linear region. The matter adsorbing at the greater relative pressures is influenced, however, by the presence of the OH groups or the complex of OH and ethyl chloride. That a complex is not essential in creating this effect is proved by the fact that butane, which shows no evidence of formation of complexes, also reveals a lower apparent polarization at higher values of adsorption.

Of interest and importance also is Shigeishi's observation that a kink reappears in the plots of ε' as a function of quantity adsorbed as the temperature of the system is lowered (see Figure 5-5). He found that the matter adsorbed at low relative pressures showed increasing loss with lowered temperature until the dielectric constant corresponded with that expected for electronic and distortion polarization only. The adsorbate in the upper layers or pores had greater orientational polarization

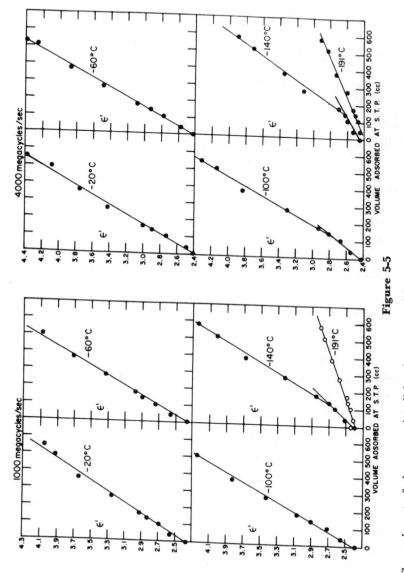

Figure 5-5

The real part of the composite dielectric constant for the system ethyl chloride–porous glass. The glass was treated to remove the majority of silanol groups. Note the elimination of a second linear section above − 100° C.

87

over a wider range of temperature, and the second linear region which became evident in the plots had a higher slope than the first linear region. Thus, as the temperature of the system is reduced, the system showed the expected behavior of a polar adsorbate such as has been found for ethyl chloride and other substances upon nonporous rutile, i.e., a low apparent polarization for material adsorbed in the first layer and a polarization more nearly that of bulk liquid for material adsorbed in the multilayers.

Shigeishi was unable to establish the mechanism by which loss is brought about, as the range of frequency was too limited. However, the value of the dielectric constant of the adsorbate was appreciably less than that for bulk liquid. Similarly the temperature coefficient of ε_2' was small in those conditions for which loss was unimportant. These characteristics suggest, but do not prove, that oscillatory motion of the adsorbed molecules is occurring, rather than free rotation. The activation energy of the process causing dielectric loss was 3.8 kcal/mole.

Some typical data are represented in Figure 5-6.

Finally, it should be stated that removal of OH groups did not eliminate the hysteresis loop of the adsorption isotherm. Further support is therefore provided for the view that hysteresis in adsorption isotherms is caused by the porous structure of the adsorbent and not by the nature of the adsorption sites.

5-6 INVESTIGATIONS BY FREYMANN AND HIS COLLABORATORS

Freymann has investigated solids containing water of crystallization, adsorbed water, and, in fact, crystalline imperfections, by means of dielectric measurements. In these studies the main techniques have involved determining the real part and the imaginary part of the dielectric constant over an

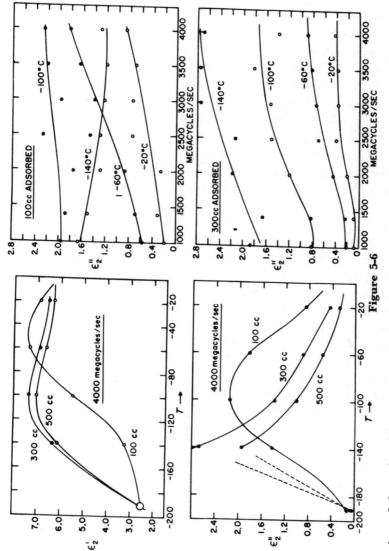

Figure 5-6

Variations of the real and imaginary parts of the dielectric constant of adsorbate for the system ethyl chloride–porous glass. The glass was treated to remove silanol groups. Part *b* of the figure shows the imaginary part as a function of frequency for the limited range 1,000 to 4,000 Mcps.

89

extended range of frequency and temperature. Where adsorbed matter has come under examination, the amount has been varied. The greatest emphasis has been placed upon the determination of loss and its variation with temperature and frequency. No attempt has been made to evaluate the characteristic of the adsorbate as such; rather, dielectric values of the composite system are reported. Loss as a function of frequency has not been exhaustively examined, because, as is evident from what has been written earlier, a very wide frequency variation must be developed for this approach to have any but limited utility. Loss maxima as a function of temperature for a variety of frequencies and adsorbate contents have been determined, and a good deal of valuable information has been accumulated. A summary of this important work from the laboratories at Rennes must now be examined.

Bulk water shows absorption of electrical energy for wavelengths on the order of centimeters, but this absorption ceases abruptly on the solidification of the liquid. Water of crystallization showed no absorption. On the other hand, adsorbed water on a variety of solids, such as alumina and silica gels and on sodium chloride, did exhibit pronounced losses down to a temperature of about −90°C (21). Le Bot and Le Montagner (36) employed several very-high-frequency (v-h-f) fields and a silica gel–water system maintained at 20°C. The gel after dehydration at 110°C revealed an absorption maximum at about 20 kMcps. When hydrated, some evidence of this maximum was believed to remain, and a further maximum at lower frequencies, and of much greater amplitude, was indicated. In view of the knowledge gained by Sidorov (24) and Folman and Yates (23), which was referred to earlier, the maximum found in the examination of the dehydrated gel may be due to the residual hydroxyl groups firmly bound to the surface. The maximum indicated in the neighborhood of 1 kMcps is presumably due to physically adsorbed water.

Rolland and Bernard obtained absorption maxima at a very much lower frequency, namely, 10 kMcps for adsorbed water on silica gel (*31*). Their important discovery was the existence of two maxima in a plot of ε'' against temperature. The first maximum at 174°K is of substantially smaller amplitude than the second, which occurred at 225°K. The gel contained an appreciable water content of some 24 per cent by weight, so that, in terms of the usual interpretation of adsorption isotherms, a condition of quite well-filled capillaries is implied.

Kamiyoshi and Odake (*20*) independently confirmed the existence of a maximum. In collaboration, Kamiyoshi and

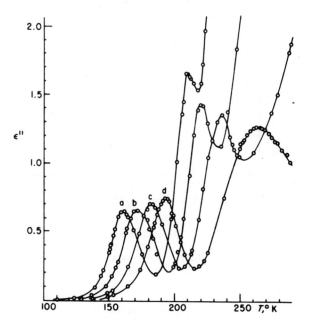

Figure 5-7

Dielectric data for a water–silica gel system obtained by Kamiyoshi and Ripoche. The existence of two maxima is clearly illustrated.

Ripoche (*32*) investigated the silica gel–water system much more thoroughly. They employed frequencies of 90 to 100,000 cps, a temperature range of 4 to 300°K, and water contents of the gel of zero to 40 per cent. Their Figure 1 is redrawn as Figure 5-7 and shows very beautifully the two maxima as a function of temperature for the various frequencies. Water content of the gel was 22.3 per cent. The temperatures of the maxima corresponding to the respective frequencies may be utilized, as has been discussed in Section 3-3B, to form a plot of $\ln \omega_m$ versus $1/T$. From the slope of this plot the activation energy H was obtained. The value of the intercept, which may be related to ω_0, was not reported. The activation energy would be expected to vary with water content of the gel, and this variation is represented in their Figure 2, which is redrawn here as Figure 5-8. The data in this case refer to the process

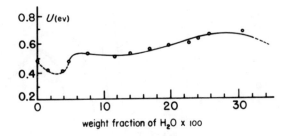

Figure 5-8

The activation energy of the loss process is shown as a function of the quantity adsorbed for the system water–silica gel.

giving rise to the low-temperature maximum. Activation energies are expressed in units of electron volts, i.e., some multiple of 23.05 kcal/mole. The magnitude of the activation energy is thus, for the low-temperature process, about 13.8 kcal/mole and, for the high-temperature process, 20.2 kcal/

mole. These figures are not greatly different from the equilibrium molar heat of adsorption of water in silica glass (4), which ranges from about 18 kcal/mole down to a value of about 10 kcal/mole near saturation. The variation of H for the low-temperature maximum with moisture content is generally positive but contains an unexplained minimum near 2 per cent water. The high-temperature maximum can be observed only between moisture contents of 7 per cent (temperature too high for lower amounts) and 24 per cent, where the maximum is no longer observed. The value of H increases uniformly with moisture content, which may illustrate an increasing inter-action between the dipoles.

There is some evidence of a small maximum at a temperature of 80°K. The maximum disappears with repeated pumping and readsorption of water. Kamiyoshi and Ripoche (32) do not attempt to explain their findings.

Rolland and Bernard (31) also brought to light the fact that the two loss maxima behave differently as water content of the gel is varied. The low-temperature maximum at 174°K remains at this temperature regardless of moisture content, whereas the high-temperature maximum decreases in magnitude and occurs at higher temperatures as the amount of adsorbate is increased. These workers suggested a dissociated form of water as the agent involved in the low-temperature maximum and associated water in the high-temperature maximum. The stationary maximum indicates adsorbate which is unaffected in properties by additions and which is comparatively less firmly bound to the substrate. Capillary condensed water could meet these requirements. The more firmly bound water indicated by the higher temperature of its loss maximum is affected by the presence of additional neighbors, and, for it, rotational loss becomes more difficult with increasing surface coverage. This result is quite the opposite of that reported by Chapman and McIntosh (10) for adsorbed ethyl chloride, which showed a diminished interaction with surface or neighbors on increasing the surface concentration.

Waldman (37) examined ethyl chloride, ammonia, water, and butane on a silica gel and ethyl chloride on nonporous rutile. The gel itself after pumping at 120°C, showed a small maximum of the loss vs. temperature plot, and the temperature of the maximum increased with increasing frequency to the highest frequency employed, namely, 1 Mcps. These observations are again explicable in terms of firmly bound polar groups such as hydroxyl groups. On addition of ethyl chloride the loss was greatly enhanced, and the temperature of maximum loss was increased. The amplitude of the loss maximum increased with higher frequency and higher temperature, as is

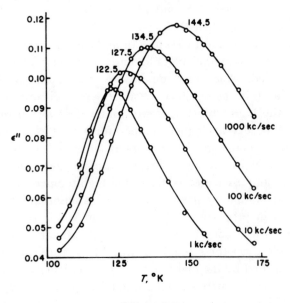

Figure 5-9

The loss maximum is shown to increase with temperature for the system ethyl chloride–Actigel. As depicted in Figure 3-2 the amplitude of the Debye type of loss would be independent of temperature.

shown in Figure 5-9. This observation, as pointed out by Waldman, is contrary to the predictions of Debye's theory, which, as seen from Figure 3-2, requires a maximum of amplitude independent of temperature. Debye's theory assumes, of course, a fixed number of dipoles of similar energies. This is probably not the case for the adsorbed ethyl chloride, since, at low temperature, some of it may be too firmly bound to take part in the process responsible for loss.

With increasing amount of adsorbed ethyl chloride, the maximum loss occurs at lower temperatures, as Chapman and McIntosh (*10*) found also with ethyl chloride on porous glass. The amplitude of the loss maximum increased with amount adsorbed. Waldman plotted the value of ε'' at the maximum against quantity adsorbed and found an abrupt change of slope at an amount adsorbed which he identified with the quantity required to complete the first layer, i.e., with V_m (see Figure 5-10).

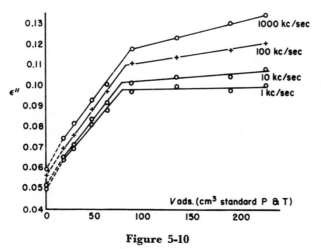

Figure 5-10

The imaginary part of the complex dielectric constant shows a sudden variation of its rate of change with quantity adsorbed. The two linear sections intersect at an amount adsorbed agreeing well with the monolayer volume. The system is ethyl chloride–Actigel.

Activation energy H also varied with amount adsorbed, from 6.9 kcal/mole for the pumped gel, through 10.0 kcal/mole for gel plus an amount of ethyl chloride less than V_m, to 7.9 kcal/mole for amounts of ethyl chloride greater than the monolayer capacity.

Ammonia exhibited a similar behavior to that of ethyl chloride, while the result of Rolland and Bernard of two maxima was confirmed with water. Butane did not enhance the loss revealed by the evacuated gel, and this finding again agrees with that of Chapman, who could find no change in the loss for butane on porous glass.

Finally, Waldman (37) reported no loss for ethyl chloride on nonporous rutile. He attributed the difference to the existence of pores in the gel. Considering, however, that very little is known concerning the energy of binding of the adsorbate to the surfaces in the two cases, it may not be justifiable to assign the difference to the porous structure. Firmly bound adsorbate might not exhibit loss in the frequency and temperature range, and a knowledge of ε'_2 in the two cases would be required to sustain the hypothesis, since a value of ε'_2 close to that of liquid material would indicate free rotation, a small value restricted rotation.

Zhilenkov (38) has investigated the water–silica gel system, and his observations are pertinent to the work of Freymann and his associates. Zhilenkov used a frequency range of 10 cps to 10 Mcps and temperatures down to $-150°C$. He obtained the value of ε_s for the composite system and the value of ε''. The activation energy involved in the process leading to loss was determined in the usual way. The value of the activation energy, whether the loss was due to conduction or to the Debye type of dispersion, had a value equivalent to that for ice down to $-100°C$, namely, 13 kcal/mole (39), at which temperature a sudden change was observed. The activation energy increased with amount adsorbed, indicating the crowding of dipoles, as has been discussed previously. The temperature of $-100°C$ is noteworthy, as it agrees with that reported by Frey-mann and Freymann (*21, 22*) as the melting point of dissociated water. Zhilenkov reported a zero temperature coefficient of ε_s until the amount adsorbed corresponded approximately to that at the beginning of the capillary condensation region, which suggests oscillatory motion of the adsorbate molecules which are first adsorbed.

5-7 HYSTERESIS IN THE ISOTHERMS AND DIELECTRIC VALUES

Hysteresis in the adsorption isotherms of porous solids has been known for a long time and studied extensively. There are two general theories which have been proposed to explain the phenomenon. The first supposes condensation in the pores at relative pressures determined by the radius of curvature of the menisci and the shape of the pores. Special forms of this view have been developed, such as the bottleneck theory due to Kraemer (*40*) and the open-ended pore theory due to Foster (*41*) and Cohan (*42*). Rules concerning the forms of scanning curves within the main loop have been developed by Katz (*43*) on the assumption of bottleneck-shaped pores. Experimental evidence in favour of the irreversible formation of menisci has been offered by Amberg and McIntosh (*4*) and by Quinn and McIntosh (*44, 45*) from studies of dimensional changes of the adsorbate-adsorbent system. The situation remains obscure, however, as evidence exists which cannot be reconciled with the capillary condensation theory, as Litvan and McIntosh have shown (*46*).

The second general theory is the independent domain theory due to Everett (*47*), which postulates assemblies of molecules which change from one state to another at a given value of the relative pressure and which revert to the former state at another value of the relative pressure. No cause is specified for this difference in the condition required to effect change. The domain theory, like the rules proposed by Katz, permits prediction of forms of scanning loops. It may be applied in conjunction with capillary condensation theory by considering groups of similar capillaries to form the domains. In this event it is possible to show that the domains are not independent (45). The capillary condensation theory remains the popular rationalization of adsorption for porous adsorbents, and is still used (48), though probably erroneously to assess pore size distributions and to estimate the mean pore size of adsorbents such as silica gel, alumina gel, activated carbon and porous glass.

Whatever the cause of hysteresis loops in adsorption isotherms, the phenomenon of time-independent hysteresis is thoroughly established. Thorp (49), Nair (50), and Fiat et al. (15) have obtained data which show hysteresis loops also in the dielectric values. The data obtained by Fiat, Folman, and Garbatski have already been discussed and are not really relevant to a discussion of time-independent hysteresis. Thorp, however, has obtained important data using methyl and ethyl alcohols as well as water, in conjunction with a silica gel, a mixed silica and ferric oxide gel, and an alumina gel. On the silica gel all three adsorbates show hysteresis in the dielectric values once a quantity adsorbed corresponding to the inception of the hysteresis loop of the adsorption isotherm has been achieved. In all cases the capacity of the test cell is greater on the adsorption branch than on the desorption branch. In the case of the mixed oxide gel the situation is reversed, so that the desorption branch reveals the greater capacities. This same observation was made for methyl and ethyl alcohols on alumina gel. Thorp attempted to explain these observations in terms of differing degrees of orientational freedom among material in the first adsorption layer, in the second adsorption layer, and the liquidlike material condensed in the capillaries, in conjunction with differing distributions of pore sizes in the three adsorbents.

More recently Nair (50), working in Thorp's laboratory, used silica gels and water as the adsorbate. The size of the capacitance loop diminished with frequency, and capacities along the adsorption branch were greater than on the desorption branch, in agreement with Thorp's result for a gel described as London Silica Commerical Gel. In contradiction to this the loop size increased with frequency and desorption points had higher capacities than adsorption points when a gel described as B.D.H. silica gel for chromatography was employed. On heating these gels to 900°C the dielectric hysteresis loop disappeared, although the adsorption isotherm loop persisted. Thus, dielectric hysteresis and pore-size distribution seem less closely connected than had been postulated by Thorp. Extreme care in washing the gels in nitric acid and many changes of distilled water was also effective in eliminating the dielectric hysteresis loop without changing apparent pore-size distribution in any way. It also reduced greatly the frequency range over which dielectric losses were observed, so that these became of consequence only below 2.5 kcps. These experiments are consistent with the postulate that an ionic migration process is involved in the hysteresis, although a completely satisfactory mechanism has not yet been proposed.

No evidence of hysteresis in dielectric values has ever been obtained in using either silica gel or porous glass in the author's laboratory, although no specific examination of water has been carried out. A special test for hysteresis was made by Petrie (35) and McCowan and McIntosh (17), using ethyl chloride as the adsorbate. The isotherm and dielectric plot are shown in Figure 5-11. McCowan (17) confirms the absence of dielectric hysteresis within the limits of the lesser precision of his apparatus. However, as the existence of dielectric hysteresis could

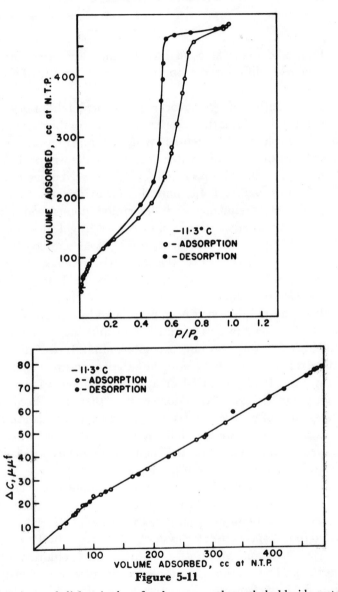

Figure 5-11

Adsorption and dielectric data for the porous glass–ethyl chloride system.
Pronounced hysteresis is observed in the adsorption data, but none is found
in the dielectric data.

100

significantly modify the views concerning adsorbed matter, further investigation is obviously required.

5-8   ADSORBED WATER ON γ-ALUMINA

Several papers have appeared recently on the dielectric properties of adsorbed water on γ-alumina. These studies confirm and extend the results which have been discussed in Sections 5-4 and 5-5.

Ebert and Langhammer (*51*) and Ebert (*52*) employed frequencies of 100 kcps to 10 Mcps, temperatures of −60 to +25°C, and a very wide range of moisture contents. The sample of γ-alumina is reported by them to have a specific surface of 97 m²/g.

The first discovery of Ebert and Langhammer was a discontinuity of slope in the plot ε' against quantity absorbed.

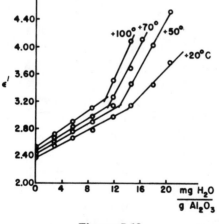

Figure 5-12

The real part of the complex dielectric constant as a function of amount adsorbed for water on γ–alumina. The sudden change of slope at low moisture content should be remarked. The change of slope occurs at an amount adsorbed which depends on frequency and temperature.

The slope increased suddenly at the critical adsorbate content, (see Figure 5-12). The change was interpreted by them, as had been done by Waldman and co-workers (53) for nonporous rutile, as marking the completion of the first adsorbed layer. As the figures which have been taken from Ebert and Lang-hammer's publication show, the position of the change is dependent upon the measuring frequency and temperature, and agreement with the BET value occurs only at the highest frequency.

As shown in Figure 5-13 taken from the same paper (51), ε' for the system increases to relatively large values with increasing moisture content. The rate of increase diminishes at about $2V_m$ for the highest temperature and frequency of 100 kcps. The diminishing rate of increase of ε' with amount adsorbed suggests reduced freedom of orientation. The low-temperature results show almost no increase of ε' with quantity adsorbed, as though no orientational freedom existed.

The loss tangent increases with amount adsorbed and much more significantly at the higher temperatures. A maximum in this plot appears for the curves from about 0°C upward, and as this has been confirmed by Baldwin and Morrow (54), this is the first establishment of that finding. Accompanying the maximum in the loss curve there is an increase in the value of ε'. Variation of temperature established a positive value of the temperature coefficient of ε'.

Hysteresis was observed in both ε' and loss tangent as a function of temperature for quantities of adsorbate in excess of 44.7 mg/g. The hysteresis loops are closed loops, and the result does not seem dependent upon the experimental procedure. The explanation may lie in a gradual phase transition over a wide range of temperature, such as has been detected also in other ways by Foote and Saxton (55) and Litvan and McIntosh (46).

Ebert (52) has also studied water in γ-alumina from -60 to

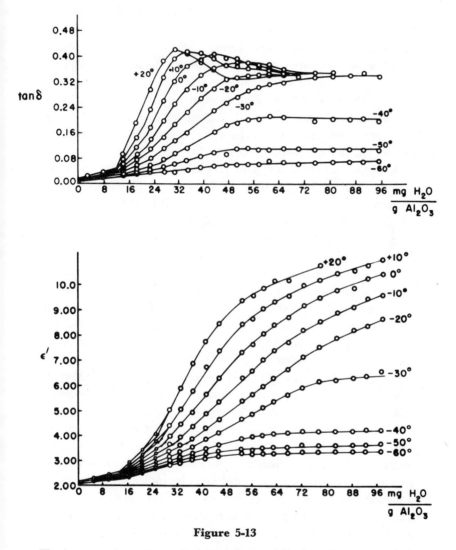

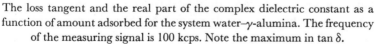

Figure 5-13

The loss tangent and the real part of the complex dielectric constant as a
function of amount adsorbed for the system water–γ-alumina. The frequency
of the measuring signal is 100 kcps. Note the maximum in tan δ.

+60°C in a quantity between the values corresponding with
V_m and $2V_m$. In this investigation loss was studied carefully as a
function of frequency, and several loss maxima were found
which were attributed to resonance phenomena. The temperature variation of the loss maximum was treated in the standard
way for the Debye type of losses, and an activation energy of
the relaxation process of 10 kcal/mole was reported. The
apparent inconsistency of treating a resonance absorption in
this way is not discussed by Ebert.

Baldwin and Morrow (54) employed frequencies between
100 cps and 100 kcps. The BET area of the sample of γ-
alumina was stated to be 270 m²/g, with nitrogen used as
adsorbate. A temperature range of 0 to 86°C was employed.
The results are in excellent agreement with those of Ebert and
Langhammer (51). A rapid increase of ε' with amount adsorbed
is reported, and the increase is greater at lower frequencies.
The rate of increase again becomes small at large values of
adsorption. The maximum of ε'' as a function of amount
adsorbed as well as the behavior of ε' are shown in Figure 5-14.

Even a qualitative explanation of these results is difficult. If
interpretation is based solely upon the orientation effects of
dipoles, there are clearly two regions in which freedom of
orientation is severely limited, namely, for the first quantities
adsorbed and for the last quantities of adsorbate. Intermediate
amounts make proportionately much greater contributions to
the polarization. It is reasonable to suppose that the first
amounts adsorbed are firmly bound and have little orientational
freedom. As amount of adsorbate is increased, successive
additions may have greater and greater freedom of movement
and may also influence the condition of the first quantities
adsorbed. If the frequency of measurement were in the correct
range, power absorption would be observed. The maximum and
subsequent disappearance of power absorption could be
explained by molecules which can turn freely, so that the

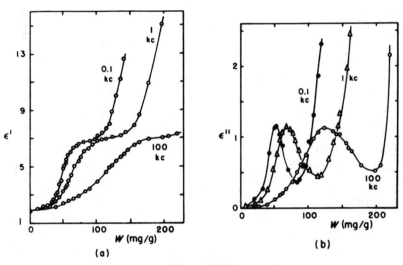

Figure 5-14

The real and imaginary parts of the complex dielectric constant for the system water–porous alumina according to Baldwin and Morrow. The maximum in the ε'' plot confirms the discovery of Ebert and Langhammer shown in Figure 5-13.

dielectric properties would be similar to those of liquid water, which would show no absorption in this frequency range. Against this interpretation, however, is the small contribution to ε', which certainly indicates a small apparent moment. In this event the explanation must lie in the crowding of the molecules as the amount adsorbed approaches saturation, and because of this crowding the freedom to orient in the applied electrical field is again reduced.

The explanation of restricted rotation for large amounts adsorbed is not consistent with the great bulk of evidence, which demonstrates the similarity of properties of adsorbates near saturation conditions to those of bulk matter. In this case it may be that the original premise, namely, dipole orientation, is inadequate. Direct-current conductivity and Maxwell-Wagner dispersion may both contribute to the power absorption and thus complicate the interpretation, although it is difficult to see why these effects should themselves cause the maximum in the power-absorption curve as a function of amount adsorbed.

Finally, if dipole orientation is retained as the postulated mechanism, the low value of loss at high adsorptions could be interpreted as meaning that the dipoles are free to rotate. On this basis an explanation of the small contribution to ε' by the adsorbed matter must be sought. In this event it may be recalled that, in porous silica gel and porous glass, polar adsorbates, including water, reveal a smaller contribution to ε' for the higher quantities adsorbed. No general explanation of this has been forthcoming, as already discussed in Section 5-2, but since the experimental result exists, it may be worthy of consideration in dealing with the new and puzzling finding due to Ebert and Langhammer (51) and to Baldwin and Morrow (54). One would thus rationalize their results by postulating firmly bound first-layer molecules and freely orienting molecules in multilayers or capillaries. The low value of ε' for the multilayer material would be explained by the "pore effect," which has been established in the cases of silica gel and porous glass.

Although a lower value of polarization seems characteristic of the matter adsorbed at higher relative pressures in porous adsorbents, the very low value of the contribution to ε' per unit of adsorbate in the results of Ebert and Langhammer and Baldwin and Morrow makes this explanation difficult to accept. Very recent results for the system HCl-NaCl, which are reported in Section 7-3, may have a bearing on the findings for the water-alumina system. Briefly, almost a zero value of ε_2' has been found for adsorbed HCl as the second layer is filling. A possible explanation of this is that the dipoles of the second layer are oriented relative to those of the first layer in a way which cancels the permanent moment of the first-layer adsorbate. This suggests that at low temperatures an ordered structure may establish itself and that this structure has a small or zero value of the permanent moment. The evidence suggesting this is represented in Figure 7-5a to d.

Dransfeld and colleagues (*56*) examined the γ-alumina–water system when a comparatively large amount of water have been adsorbed on the porous substrate. Their aim was to establish the freezing mechanism of the adsorbed water through a study of relaxation time. The relaxation time was observed by means of the frequency at which the loss maximum occurred as temperature was varied from the lowest values up to 100°K. For higher temperatures than this a v-h-f signal of 58 kMcps was used so that the condition $\omega\tau \gg 1$ was met and loss and relaxation time are directly related [see (1-5)]. The results showed a single maximum in the loss when plotted against temperature, occurring at about 200°K. A continuous variation of $1/\tau$ with temperature was revealed. Thus adsorbed water was considered to exist as a single phase, rather than as many phases of distinct properties in capillaries of different dimensions. On cooling, the adsorbate was considered to exist as an undercooled liquid and at the lowest temperatures as a glass.

It is interesting to note here that Higuti (*57*) followed the dielectric behavior of nitrobenzene in silica gel and observed a discontinuity in the slope of the capacity-change vs. amount-adsorbed plot at different quantities adsorbed for different temperatures. He attributed the phenomenon to the freezing of adsorbed matter in capillaries and used, in a later paper, the capillary-condensation theory and the Kelvin formula to relate the freezing temperature to the capillary radius (*58*). A continuous range of capillary sizes would permit observation of a continuous range of relaxation times.

Higuti's results (see Figure 5-15) are also of interest in connection with the observations of ε' discussed earlier in this

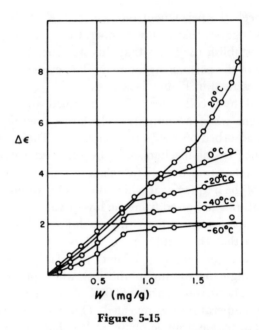

Figure 5-15

Data for the nitrobenzene–silica gel system. Loss of orientational freedom is clearly shown to occur at reduced temperatures.

section. The major difference consists in the fact that Higuti observed only one region of small slope, while Ebert and Langhammer observed two such regions. Some useful references to the freezing of adsorbates may be found in a recent paper by Litvan (*46*).

REFERENCES

1. I. Higuti, *Bull. Inst. Phys. Chem. Research Tokyo,* **20**, 489 (1941).
2. L. N. Kurbatov, *Russian J. Phys. Chem.* (*English Transl.*), **24**, 899 (1950).
3. R. McIntosh, H. Johnson, N. Hollies, and L. McLeod, *Can. J. Research,* **B25**, 566 (1947).

4. C. H. Amberg and R. McIntosh, *Can. J. Chem.*, **30**, 1012 (1952).

5. C. Hodgson and R. McIntosh, *Can. J. Chem.*, **38**, 958 (1960).

6. J. A. Morrison and L. E. Drain, *J. Chem. Phys.*, **19**, 1063 (1951).

7. P. H. Emmett and S. Brunauer, *J. Am. Chem. Soc.*, **57**, 2732 (1935).

8. W. A. Patrick and W. E. Land, *J. Phys. Chem.*, **38**, 1201 (1934).

9. R. McIntosh, E. K. Rideal, and J. A. Snelgrove, *Proc. Roy. Soc. (London)*, **A208**, 292 (1951).

10. I. Chapman and R. McIntosh, *Can. J. Chem.*, **40**, 92 (1962).

11. J. Snelgrove, H. Greenspan, and R. McIntosh, *Can. J. Chem.*, **31**, 72 (1953).

12. S. Brunauer, P. H. Emmett, and E. Teller, *J. Am. Chem. Soc.*, **60**, 309 (1938).

13. C. Pierce, J. W. Wiley, and R. N. Smith, *J. Phys. Colloid Chem.*, **53**, 669 (1949).

14. W. D. Harkins, "Colloid Chemistry," Vol. VI, Chap. 1, Reinhold, New York, 1946.

14a. G. C. Benson, E. W. Channen, and R. McIntosh, *J. Colloid Sci.*, **11**, 593 (1956).

15. D. Fiat, M. Folman, and U. Garbatski, *Proc. Roy. Soc. (London)*, **A260**, 409 (1961).

16. E. Petrie and R. McIntosh, *Can. J. Chem.*, **35**, 183 (1957).

17. J. D. McCowan and R. McIntosh, *Can. J. Chem.*, **39**, 425 (1961).

18. S. Kurosaki, *J. Phys. Chem.*, **58**, 320 (1954).

19. R. W. Sillars, *J. IEE*, **80**, 378 (1937).

20. K. Kamiyoshi and T. Odake, *Sci. Rept. Res. Inst. Tohoku Univ.*, **A5**, 271 (1953).

21. M. Freymann and R. Freymann, *Compt. Rend.*, **232**, 40 (1951).

22. M. Freymann and R. Freymann, *Compt Rend.*, **232**, 1096 (1951).

23. M. Folman and D. J. C. Yates, *Trans. Faraday Soc.*, **54**, 1684 (1958).

24. A. N. Sidorov, *Russian J. Phys. Chem. (English Transl.)*, **30**, 183 (1956).

25. H. Fröhlich, "Theory of Dielectrics: Dielectric Constants and Dielectric Loss," pp. 9ff., Clarendon Press, Oxford, 1949.

26. B. D. Ripley and R. McIntosh, *Can. J. Chem.*, **39**, 526 (1961).

27. L. Onsager, *J. Am. Chem. Soc.*, **58**, 1486 (1936).

28. M. Folman, Microwave Studies of Adsorbed Molecules, *Technion Rept.*, Israel Institute of Technology, Haifa, Israel, 1962.

29. U. Feldman, C. H. Schonfeld, and M. Folman, *Trans. Faraday Soc.*, **59**, 2394 (1963).

30. I. Lubezky, U. Feldman, and M. Folman, *Trans. Faraday Soc.*, **61**, 940 (1965).

31. M. Rolland and R. Bernard, *Compt. Rend.*, **232** ,1098 (1951).

32. K. Kamiyoshi and J. Ripoche, *J. Phys. Radium.*, **19**, 943 (1958).

33. N. W. Cant and L. H. Little, *Can. J. Chem.*, **42**, 802 (1964).

34. R. Shigeishi, Thesis, Queen's University, Kingston, Ontario, Canada, 1965.

35. E. Petrie, Thesis, University of Toronto, 1957.

36. J. Le Bot and S. Le Montagner, *Compt. Rend.*, **233**, 862 (1951).

37. M. Waldman, *Compt. Rend.*, **17**, 426 (1956).

38. V. Zhilenkov, *Izv. Acad. Nauk SSSR Otdel. Khim. Nauk*, **245**, (1957).

39. M. Freymann and R. Freymann, *J. Phys. Radium.*, **15**, 217 (1954).

40. E. O. Kraemer, *in* " A Treatise on Physical Chemistry " (H. S. Taylor, ed.), Van Nostrand, Princeton, N.J., 1942.

41. A. G. Foster, *Trans. Faraday Soc.*, **28**, 645 (1932).

42. L. H. Cohan, *J. Am. Chem. Soc.*, **60**, 433 (1938).

43. S. M. Katz, *J. Phys. Colloid Chem.*, **53**, 1166 (1949).

44. H. W. Quinn and R. McIntosh, *Can. J. Chem.*, **35**, 745 (1957).

45. H. W. Quinn and R. McIntosh, *Proc. Intern. Conf. Surface Activity Second*, London ,1957.

46. G. Litvan and R. McIntosh, *Can. J. Chem.*, **41**, 3095 (1963).

47. D. H. Everett, *Trans. Faraday Soc.*, **50**, 1077 (1954).

48. R. F. Feldman and P. J. Sereda, *J. Appl. Chem.*, **13**, 158 (1963).

49. J. M. Thorp, *Trans. Faraday Soc.*, **55**, 442 (1959).

50. N. K. Nair, private communication, 1964.

51. G. Ebert and G. Langhammer, *Kolloid Z.*, **174**, 5, (1961).

52. G. Ebert, *Kolloid Z.*, **184**, 148 (1962).

53. M. Waldman, J. A. Snelgrove, and R. McIntosh, *Can. J. Chem.*, **31**, 998 (1953).

54. M. G. Baldwin and J. C. Morrow, *J. Chem. Phys.*, **36**, 1591 (1962).

55. H. W. Foote and B. Saxton, *J. Am. Chem. Soc.*, **38**, 588 (1916).

56. K. Dransfeld, H. L. Frisch, and E. A. Wood, *J. Chem. Phys.*, **36**, 1574 (1962).

57. I. Higuti, *Sci. Rept. Res. Inst. Tohoku Univ.*, **33**, 174 (1949).

58. I. Higuti, *Sci. Rept. Res. Inst. Tohoku Univ.*, **33**, 231 (1949).

CHAPTER 6

EFFECT OF SORBED

MATTER ON POLYMERS,

CELLULOSE, STARCH, AND PROTEINS

6-1 INTRODUCTION

A very large body of experimental information has been
accumulated on the effect of adsorbates, particularly water, on
the dielectric properties of this class of long-chain molecule.

Since the substrate frequently interacts strongly with the adsorbate, as is shown, for example, by changes of volume, the situation is more complex than the cases of nonporous solids and rigid gels. It is thus more difficult to interpret the data, and therefore a very small number of papers will be reviewed in the present chapter, in fact only a sufficient number to illustrate the possibilities of the method and to show the similarities and differences between the systems described earlier and these important but complex systems.

6-2 WATER-TERYLENE SYSTEM

The water-terylene system was systematically studied by Reddish (1), who distinguished three dielectric processes, namely, relaxation of dipoles along the main polymer chain, orientation of hydroxyl groups, and an l-f and high-temperature conduction. The loss process in the dry polymer was attributed to OH groups, and adsorbed water was considered to behave in the same way as these. Addition of water increased both ε' and ε''. The frequency of the maximum loss did not change with quantity of water.

A comparison of the effect of water upon crystalline and amorphous terylene led to the conclusion that adsorbed water in the partially amorphous sample brought about loss because of OH groups located in the amorphous regions and that terminal OH groups in the crystalline regions do not contribute to the loss. The activation energy of the relaxation process was determined in the usual way and led to a value of 12.4 kcal/mole.

6-3 CELLULOSE

Seidman and Mason (2) are among those who have investigated the effects of adsorbates on cellulose. Their contribution is notable for the use of water, methanol, and ethanol as adsorbates and for their attempt to evaluate the dielectric characteristics of the fiber alone. The conditions employed involved a frequency range of 30 cps to 1 Mcps, a temperature range of -60 to $+30°C$, and amounts of sorbate up to 7 per cent by weight. The values of the parts of the complex dielectric constant of the fiber were obtained by the use of formulas due to Argue and Maass (3).

The temperature coefficient of ε' (composite dielectric) was always positive, and a maximum of ε'' was found at some temperature T_m. For fixed moisture content, decreased frequency reduced the value of T_m and brought about an increase in ε' at a particular temperature. The value of ε' increased regularly with addition of water, and a similar result was found for ε''. The most important result was the shift of T_m to lower values as the water content was increased. This result was interpreted by Seidman and Mason as a demonstration of the increased ease of rotation of the dipoles.

Methanol and ethanol brought about changes similar to those produced by adsorbed water. The effect of these adsorbates on the maximum loss was found to be about the same for each substance if compared on the basis of a common amount of sorbed OH group. A further similarity among the three in the adsorbed state was shown by evaluating the enthalpies, free energies, and entropies of activation from the variation of loss with temperature. The enthalpy of activation for water varied from 11.8 to 9.5 kcal/mole, for methanol from 10.3 to 8.7 kcal/mole, and for ethanol from 10.2 to 8.6 kcal/mole. The free energy of activation for all three substances suggests a peculiar condition represented in the case of methanol at 2.7 per cent by weight adsorbate, and this situation apparently is detectable from density measurements or refractive-index measurements of native fibers.

6-4 STARCH

An excellent example of the information to be gained by
dielectric studies is represented by the work of Ono and co-
workers (4) on the starch-water system. Both the α and β
modifications were investigated and do not differ appreciably
in their behavior. Two frequency ranges, 500 cps to 30 kcps
and 190 kcps to 3 Mcps, were utilized. An l-f loss process was
discovered which could not be identified with certainty as a
Debye loss, as d-c and Maxwell-Wagner losses could have
contributed significantly to the total loss. The positive value
of the temperature coefficient of ε' was clearly established, and
a loss maximum at about $-50°C$, which was considered to
result from an h-f process at higher temperatures. The activation
energy of the loss process was found to range between 15 and
12 kcal/mole as the moisture content increased. A differential
specific polarization was evaluated according to the method
outlined in Section 2-4C. Values of the differential specific
polarization increased regularly with increasing water content
from 12.1 to 23.2 cc/g (see Figure 6-1), whereas the value of
liquid water is 17.7 cc/g. Another case is thus presented in
which a polarization greater than that of bulk material must
be explained. Ono, Kuge, and Koizumi suggested two possibilities. One was the development of hydrogen bonds, and the
other was the loosening of the starch structure, with consequent enhancement of the freedom of rotation of polar groups
in the starch molecule.

The higher-frequency studies permitted the examination of
the loss maximum in further detail. The temperature at which
the loss maximum occurred for a fixed frequency was lowered
by increased moisture content. The amplitude and breadth of
the maximum of the loss curve as a function of frequency
altered significantly with varying temperature. The usual

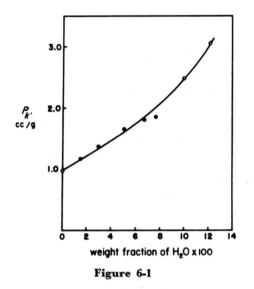

Figure 6-1

The specific polarization is shown as a function of amount adsorbed for the system water–starch.

practice of computing enthalpies, free energies, and entropies of activation was followed and led to values for ΔH between 10.6 and 12.6 kcal/mole as a function of increasing water content for β-starch; α-starch gave a range of 10.9 to 11.5 kcal/mole, which, in view of the experimental uncertainty, is probably the same as for the β-modification.

The variation of the amplitude of the loss maximum with temperature and the increasing value of the low frequency ε' with temperature caused Ono, Kuge, and Koizumi to consider the possibility of an order-disorder transition as discussed in Section 3-3B on the basis of Fröhlich's development. Quantitative testing was not attempted, but qualitative agreement with the theory was claimed.

6-5 PROTEINS

Rosen's paper (*5*) on the effect of adsorbed water on the dielectric properties of protein powders is a further example of the value of such studies. Several proteins were examined, namely, bovine serum albumin, silk fibroin, β-casein, and sperm whale myoglobin. All measurements were carried out for the temperature range 18 to 22°C, but moisture content was varied up to 0.37 weight fraction and frequency from 50 kcps to 20 Mcps. The value of ε' is represented as a function of water content for three frequencies in Figure 6-2, which is

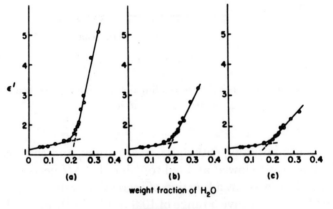

Figure 6-2

ε' as a function of moisture content at 10^5, 10^6, and 10^7cps, respectively. The adsorbent is bovine serum albumin.

Figure 2 of Rosen's paper. Conductance was examined as a function of frequency in order to evaluate ε'' from the linear part of the plot which resulted after frequencies above 2 Mcps had been attained. These constant values of ε'' are represented as a function of the weight fraction of water in Figure 6-3, which is Rosen's Figure 3*b*. A similar set of data is represented for silk fibroin in Figure 6-4, which is Rosen's Figure 4.

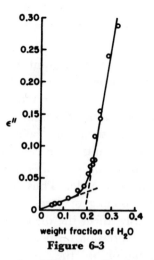

Figure 6-3

ε'' for frequencies greater than 2 Mcps as a function of hydration for bovine serum albumin.

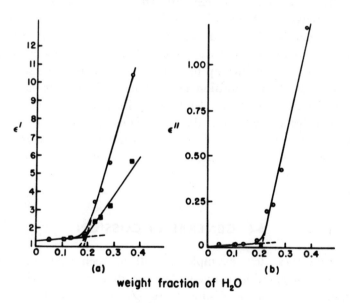

(a) **(b)**

weight fraction of H₂O

Figure 6-4

Dielectric data for water in silk fibroin ε' at 10^5 cps (◯) and at 10^6 cps (■) ε'' at frequencies greater than 2×10^6 cps.

From such data several important facts emerge. First, a critical quantity of adsorbed water was found which may be regarded as firmly bound to the protein molecule and which may be considered to measure the number of polar adsorption sites and to form a unimolecular layer of adsorbed water. Second, experimental results were not dependent upon the treatment of the protein before water was adsorbed and the dielectric measurements made. Thus air baking of bovine serum albumin and boiling of a solution of the material in water did not seriously affect the dielectric results. Third, the Onsager-Kirkwood expression for polarization in Section 2-4B, permitted an evaluation of the molecular polarization of both the protein and the adsorbed water. The molecular polarization of the protein differed from one protein to the other between about 8.5×10^{-21} to about 2.5×10^{-21} cm^3. Water exhibited a value of about 1.5×10^{-23} cm^3 for the amounts below the critical quantity, i.e., for the firmly bound adsorbate, and values up to thirty times greater for the water outside the first hydration layer. Such values were noted in comparison with 12.7×10^{-23} cm^3 in liquid water at low frequencies for which a dielectric constant of 81 would be measured and 0.7×10^{-23} cm^3 in liquid water at very high frequencies for which a dielectric constant of about 5 would be found for bulk liquid.

6-6 GENERAL DISCUSSION

From these few examples it will be seen that somewhat similar information is available from dielectric studies in the case of large molecule-adsorbate systems as in the case of rigid gel systems. Increases of ε' are observed in both types of system which are dependent upon the quantity of added adsorbate. The situation revealed is that the first quantities of adsorbate are firmly bound, either because they make up the first molecular layer or because they are adsorbed upon polar parts of the substrate. If the binding is very strong, a low value of polarization of the adsorbate is observed. Increase in the amount of adsorbate gives evidence of weaker interaction through increasing ε' with quantity of adsorbate. A positive temperature coefficient of ε' may be observed which may be interpreted as a greater number of dipoles capable of orientation in the applied field or as evidence of an order-disorder transition. Similar conclusions result from variations of ε''. Firmly bound adsorbate shows appreciable loss only at low frequencies or at high temperature. Weakening of interaction with the substrate is shown by the shifting of a loss maximum to higher frequencies or to lower temperatures. Activation energies of the relaxation process are on the order of 10 to 15 kcal/mole both for gel systems on the one hand, and polymers or proteins on the other, for adsorbates containing hydroxyl groups. These values are in the range anticipated for physical adsorption forces and not chemical bonding.

Polarization of the adsorbate has been calculated in a variety of ways, and sometimes the value is much in excess of the polarization of bulk liquid. In this event rationalization has been attempted from the view point either of induced dipoles being created, or of an effect upon the substrate which permits orientation of dipolar groups which were incapable of orientation before the addition of the adsorbate. Caution must be exercised in this connection, however, for, as has been repeatedly stressed, all procedures for calculating polarization are doubtful, and the advance of this type of study has been seriously impeded by this fact. Nevertheless, an increased understanding of adsorbate-adsorbent systems has been achieved which, in some cases, has been more than qualitative.

REFERENCES

1. W. Reddish, *Trans. Faraday Soc.*, **46**, 459 (1950).
2. R. Seidman and S. G. Mason, *Can. J. Chem.*, **32**, 744 (1954).
3. G. H. Argue and O. Maass, *Can. J. Research*, **B13**, 156 (1935).
4. S. Ono, T. Kuge, and N. Koizumi, *Bull. Chem. Soc. Japan*, **31**, 34 (1958).
5. D. Rosen, *Trans. Faraday Soc.*, **59**, 2178 (1963).

CHAPTER 7

ADSORBATES ON NONPOROUS SOLIDS

7-1 INTRODUCTION

In Section 5-1 it was pointed out that few experimental investigations of nonporous solids have been attempted. The paramount difficulty is the preparation of the solid, which must have a large specific surface and which must be a non-conductor. The latter requirement eliminates investigations of carbons of high surface area which are available. Up to the present a rutile of specific surface 85 m²/g and a sodium chloride sample of specific surface about 30 m²/g are the two nonporous solids which have been examined. The earlier and more extensive work involves the rutile substrate, and the results obtained using this will be presented and discussed first.

7-2 BUTANE AND SOME POLAR ADSORBATES ON NONPOROUS RUTILE

Butane was employed with porous adsorbents as a convenient nonpolar adsorbate; thus, it was expected to yield easily explicable properties, as complications due to orientational polarization should be absent. It was therefore tried with rutile and, as shown in Figure 7-1, gave rise to a simple linear relation between the increase of capacity of the test cell and the quantity adsorbed until about three times the quantity required to complete the unimolecular layer had been adsorbed. The dielectric constant calculated by using Equation (2-13) was 2.05, i.e., somewhat higher than the value from the refractive index, namely, 1.80. As Böttcher's powder method is not satisfactory for a powder of such high dielectric constant as rutile, and as the assumption of liquid-state density of the adsorbate and the small change of capacity may be involved in the accuracy of the derived value of the dielectric constant, as well as a contribution from atomic polarization, the value of 2.05 was considered to show that adsorbed butane has dielectric properties identical with those in its bulk state. No detectable change of dielectric constant is revealed on the completion of the unimolecular layer, this fact being in contrast with the behavior of polar adsorbates.

Data obtained with the same rutile and three polar adsorbates are also illustrated in Figure 7-1. Two temperatures were employed in each case so that a comparison is shown of behavior for temperatures differing by about 25 degrees. In all these cases the capacitance change as a function of quantity adsorbed

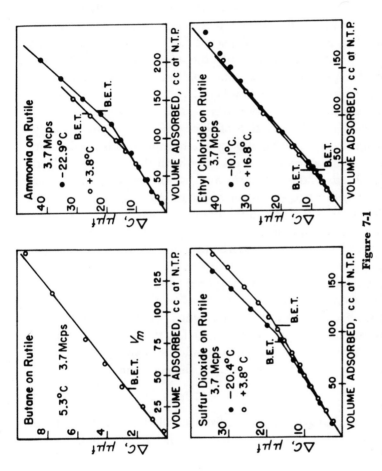

Figure 7-1

The behavior of a nonpolar and several polar adsorbates when adsorbed on nonporous rutile. The sudden increase of polarization after the completion of the monolayer should be noted.

123

consists of two linear sections. The first section always has the lower slope. In the case of ammonia no temperature coefficient of the slope is observable. Indeed, as shown in Table 7-1, the computed value of the dielectric constant is virtually independent of temperature for all three adsorbates. The absolute value of ε_2 is below that expected for the liquid state. These two facts are consistent with the view that the adsorbed molecules are behaving as rotational oscillators provided that they are adsorbed in the first layer.

The second linear section has a greater slope than the first and also a greater variation of slope with temperature. Fairly good agreement is revealed between the amount adsorbed at the beginning of the second linear section with the V_m value derived from the adsorption isotherm and use of the BET multilayer theory. The least good agreement occurs in the case of ammonia, but in this case the adsorption data were least well represented by the BET equation. On the basis of the approximate correspondence of these adsorbed quantities, the greater slope is characteristic of material adsorbed in the multilayers. Such material has a greater orientational polarization and in fact seems to have dielectric properties like those of bulk liquid. Again the exception is ammonia, which shows a much greater dielectric constant than that predicted by the Onsager equation. In this connection, however, it should be pointed out that for comparatively large values of C_2 in the equation

$$4\pi C_2/3 = (\varepsilon_2 - 1)/(\varepsilon_2 + 2)$$

very large changes of ε_2 result from small changes of C_2. Thus a change of about 15 per cent in C_2 is sufficient to account for the difference between a dielectric constant of 17 and one of 69. Errors as high as 15 per cent are unlikely in the slope of the line which establishes the value of C_2, but the very large values of ε_2 are probably in part attributable to experimental error. By and large the data indicate a lower value of ε_2 than bulk

TABLE 7-1

Dielectric Constants of Gases on Nonporous Rutile
Specific surface 84 m²/g

Gas	Temp., °C	Frequency, Mcps	ε_2, first section	ε_2, second section	ε_2, third section	ε, liquid	Discontinuity of slope, cc/g at NTP	BET V_m, cc/g at NTP
n-Butane	−7.6	3.7	2.0₅	—	—	2.03	—	7.5
Ethyl chloride	−50.0	92.0	6.7	10.9	—	14.2	8.1	6.9
	−29.0	92.0	6.8	10.9	—	12.6	7.4	7.7
	−9.0	92.0	6.8	9.2	—	11.1	7.2	7.2
	9.0	92.0	6.6	8.9	—	9.9	7.0	6.9
	0.6	3.7	6.7	7.6	—	10.4	7.5	7.5
	9.2	3.7	6.4	7.4	—	9.9	7.9	8.7
	−33.0	89.0	6.1	8.1	—	12.7	8.7	7.7
	−49.0	89.0	6.5	8.8	—	14.2	8.7	8.4
Ammonia	−23.0	3.7	15.6	55 ± 15	—	16.7	21.6	24.6
	3.8	3.7	16.7	29 ± 5	—	14.0	13.3	24.0
Sulfur dioxide	−20.4	3.7	8.3	14.8	—	16.6	16.9	18.8
	−5.0	3.7	9.3	11.4	—	15.5	15.0	12.1
	3.8	3.7	8.1	10.8	—	14.8	21.6	18.9
Dichlorofluoro-methane	−50.0	92.0	4.8	7.2	—	7.9	8.5	8.5
	−30.0	92.0	4.8	7.3	—	7.3	8.2	7.7
	−19.6	3.7	4.8	7.1	—	6.9	7.7	7.9
	0.0	92.0	5.0	5.5	—	6.1	7.7	7.2
	9.0	92.0	5.3	5.3	—	5.9	—	—
	20.2	3.7	5.1	5.4	—	5.4	7.7	7.9
1,1,1-difluoro-chloroethane	−20.3	3.7	7.9	5.6	9.0	12.4	8.7	8.6
	−19.0	3.7	7.9	5.7	9.2	12.3	8.7	8.7
	−2.0	3.7	7.8	5.4	8.7	11.0	8.6	8.6
	10.1	3.7	7.9	5.5	8.8	10.1	8.6	8.4

liquid for the first section and a value consistent with the liquid state of aggregation for the second region. Temperature coefficients support this conclusion.

Petrie (*1*) examined dichlorofluoromethane using the type of cell shown in Figure 4-3 and a measuring frequency of 92 Mcps. The results are illustrated in Figure 7-2, and examination of the figure will show the same slope for the first linear sections in spite of the fact that the temperatures differed by 59 degrees.

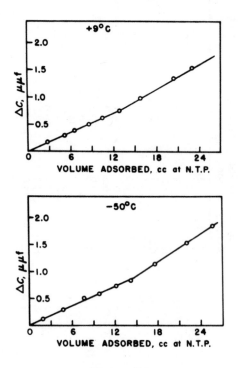

Figure 7-2

The behavior of dichlorofluoromethane on nonporous rutile is shown at two well-separated values of temperature. There is no temperature coefficient along the first section. A negative temperature coefficient is found along the second section. Frequency of the measuring signal was 92 Mcps.

The slopes of the second linear sections reveal a negative temperature coefficient. A similar result for a 40-degree variation of temperature is shown in Figure 7-3 for the same adsorbate and a measuring frequency of 3.7 Mcps.

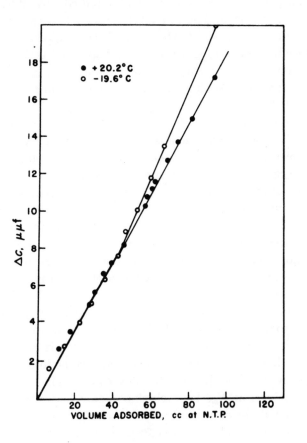

Figure 7-3

Dichlorofluoromethane adsorbed on nonporous rutile at two temperatures. The temperature coefficient of the second linear section is clearly revealed. Frequency of the measuring signal was 3.7 Mcps.

Loss was not observed for any adsorbate on the nonporous adsorbent even at the lowest temperature and highest frequency. These conditions were those stated above for dichlorofluoromethane, namely, $-50°C$ and 92 Mcps. As mentioned in Section 5-6 Waldman (2) also studied ethyl chloride on nonporous rutile and found no loss. The highest frequency employed by him was 1 Mcps, but lower temperatures were employed. These temperatures are not specified in Waldman's paper, but if the procedure employed was the same as for the studies involving Actigel, the lowest temperature could have been 150°K.

Figure 7-4 shows data obtained by Petrie (1) for the adsorbate 1,1,1-difluorochloroethane adsorbed at about $-20°C$ and with a measuring signal of 3.7 Mcps. There is little doubt that the data reveal three linear sections of the capacitance change as a function of amount adsorbed. The first has a higher value than the second, and both these sections are observed before the V_m value of adsorption is achieved. This was the first case among the systems which have been studied in the author's laboratory for which a changed value of polarization is observed as the unimolecular layer is completed. It is tempting to interpret the lower slope of the second section as due to dipole-dipole interaction and the abrupt change to a mechanism similar to the suggestion of Roberts (3) of nearest-neighbor repulsions on a lattice which forms a square array. When the lattice is half filled, repulsive interactions come into play, with a sudden drop of the heat of adsorption. The third linear section begins at V_m. Its high slope again suggests increased orientational freedom in the multilayers. However, the slope of this section is about equal to that of the first section, and since temperature variation of the apparent dielectric constant was not investigated over an extended range, little further can be said.

Before summarizing the conclusions which have been reached

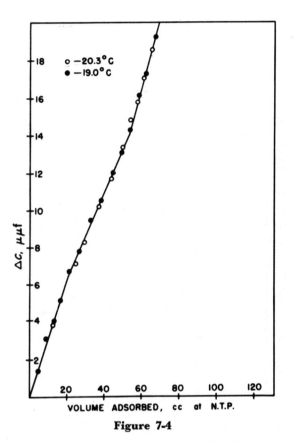

Figure 7-4

Difluorochloroethane adsorbed upon nonporous rutile. There are two linear sections before completion of the monolayer. The beginning of the third section corresponds well with the monolayer capacity.

through the study of nonporous rutile, a further comment upon the absolute values of ε'_2 is warranted. It has already been stated that Böttcher's powder method does not yield correct values of the dielectric constant of the substrate, and because of this the cluster treatment was developed and employed in some cases. Table 7-2 shows a comparison of values of ε'_2 for ethyl

TABLE 7-2

Comparison of Cluster Method and Extended Böttcher Method for Ethyl Chloride

(Adsorbent rutile specific surface 85 m²/g)

Böttcher method		Temp., °C	Cluster method	
ε_2, first section	ε_2, second section		ε_2, first section	ε_2, second section
6.7	7.6	0.6	6.8	8.3
5.7	7.1	9.2	5.4	7.5
6.4	7.4	9.2	6.8	8.5
6.5	8.8	−49.0	6.8	8.9
6.1	8.1	−33.0	6.5	8.2
6.0	8.2	−17.0	6.4	8.2
5.9	8.1	9.0	6.3	7.6

chloride adsorbed upon rutile when the extended Böttcher method and the cluster method were used. It is seen that there is excellent agreement between the two. On this basis there is again evidence that the initial dielectric reading for the powdered substrate alone does not influence greatly the calculated value for the adsorbate.

With this comment in mind, the results for nonporous rutile may be generalized. First, a nonpolar adsorbate such as butane behaves as one would anticipate from its bulk properties, and no discrimination of first-layer or multilayer adsorption is revealed by the dielectric data. Second, all polar adsorbates show at least two linear sections of the dielectric data. A sudden change of apparent polarization occurs at a quantity adsorbed which the multilayer-adsorption theory reveals as the amount required to complete the monolayer. Third, the first quantities of adsorbate behave in a manner which is consistent with prediction for a rotational oscillator in a plane; i.e., a negligible temperature coefficient of ε_2' is found as well as a value of ε_2' which is appreciably less than would be predicted on the basis of bulk-liquid properties. Fourth, the linear section which occurs for quantities of adsorbate greater than V_m shows a negative temperature coefficient and a higher value of ε_2' which is not much less than for bulk liquid. Fifth, a single case has been revealed of an adsorbate showing a sudden change of apparent polarization before the completion of the monolayer.

Finally, comment is required upon the excellent linearity of the plots of capacitance change as a function of quantity adsorbed. Apparently, in spite of the probable heterogeneous nature of the surface and the likelihood of dipole-dipole interactions, there is no evidence of variation of the apparent moment in the experimental results. This observation seems inconsistent with known variations of the differential heat of adsorption, although these data have not been computed for the systems of which the dielectric properties have been studied. A possible explanation of this is a lack of sensitivity of the dielectric property. However, the data for 1,1,1-difluorochloroethane and for hydrogen chloride on salt deny this rationalization and indicate that changes of dielectric characteristics may be recognized when they occur.

7-3 HYDROGEN CHLORIDE ON NONPOROUS SODIUM CHLORIDE

The theoretical treatment of a dipolar molecule which is constrained to undergo rotational oscillations in a plane parallel to the surface, attempted for a dipole resembling hydrogen chloride on a sodium chloride surface by Benson et al. (4), encouraged the experimental investigation of that system. Preliminary observations were made by Crozier (5) and McMullen in the author's laboratory. The dielectric cell is shown in Figure 4-1. Even with vibration of the cell during filling with the powdered salt,* a packing density of only 0.22 g/cc was achieved. In consequence of this, comparatively small quantities of gas were adsorbed, and small changes of the capacitance of the test cell were observed. Nevertheless, as eight frequencies were examined by means of the Schering bridge and several higher frequencies by means of a resonant circuit, there can be little doubt concerning the validity of the results. In all, a frequency range of 3 kcps to 8 Mcps was employed, and three temperatures were utilized, namely, $-70°$, $-90°$, and $-110°C$. No evidence was found of an h-f loss due to the adsorbate. An l-f loss does occur which is dependent upon the amount adsorbed but which is of very small magnitude.

*The salt was kindly prepared by Mr. Darcy in Dr. G. C. Benson's laboratory in the Division of Pure Chemistry of the National Research Council, Ottawa. The procedure was essentially that employed by Craig and McIntosh (6) and by Young and Morrison (7).

At $-110°C$ the adsorption isotherm was type II in the usual Brunauer classification, and adsorption was conveniently followed to about $3V_m$. However, at the two higher temperatures the lower values of relative pressure which result from a maximum experimental pressure of 1 atm did not permit adsorption to be studied beyond about $1.8V_m$ at $-70°C$ and $2.7V_m$ at $-90°C$. The isotherm at $-110°C$ is shown in Figure 7-5a, and the reproducibility of successive experiments is clearly demonstrated. Some uncertainty concerning the choice of the best straight-line section in the plots used to obtain V_m from the multilayer form of the adsorption isotherms limited the definition of V_m to between 110 and 130 cc at NTP without any regular variation with temperature. The result, however, is of significance in relation to the plots of capacitance change as a function of quantity adsorbed which are represented in Figure 7-5b, c, and d.

At the lowest temperature of $-110°C$ the first part of the plot is similar to those obtained for the majority of polar adsorbates on nonporous rutile. The two linear sections are familiar, as is the lower value of slope of the first section in comparison with that of the second. The qualitative interpretation offered earlier remains useful, and one would postulate rotational oscillations of the adsorbate in the first layer and Debye behavior in the second and higher layers. In agreement with this postulate is the position of the sudden change of slope which occurs close to the V_m value of adsorption.

Although a nonlinear section of the plot of capacitance change as a function of quantity adsorbed seems required for the data obtained at $-70°C$, it is possible to distinguish a much lower variation of slope with temperature for the sections representing the adsorption into the monolayer than for the second-layer adsorption. This fact is also consistent with the postulate of molecular motion being that of rotational oscillators. Second-layer adsorbate shows an appreciable variation

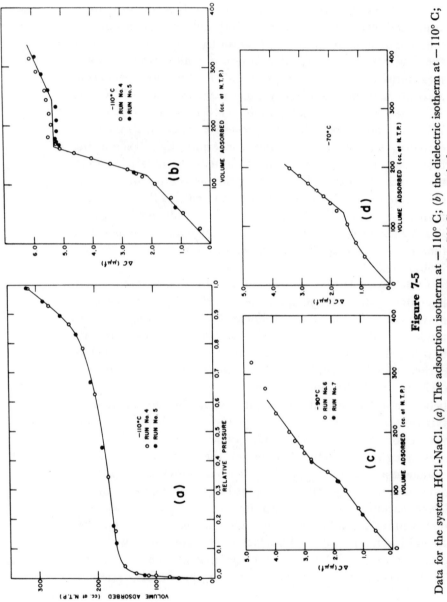

Figure 7-5

Data for the system HCl-NaCl. (a) The adsorption isotherm at −110° C; (b) the dielectric isotherm at −110° C; (c, d) the dielectric isotherms at −90 and −70° C, respectively.

134

of its dielectric properties with temperature over the range of temperature in which a distinct section attributable to second-layer adsorption can be recognized, namely, -110 to $-90°$C. The data for the second section of the $-70°$C plot probably represent the average property of second- and multilayer material, as the successive filling of layers is becoming less discernible with increased temperature.

The horizontal section of the plot representing data of the $-110°$C isotherm requires comment. The validity of this section is less firmly established than that of the other sections. Some unknown factor causes the reproducibility of the dielectric data to be less in this section than in others, although there is no evidence of poor reproducibility in the adsorption isotherm. Even with this precautionary remark in mind, it is safe to state that a region exists in which polarizable material is added to a capacitor without appreciable increase in its capacitance. In these circumstances it must be assumed that the added matter is affecting the polarization of adsorbate already present in such a way that the net effect is essentially a zero increment in polarization. It is to be noted that this result is found in the absence of any dielectric loss. Cancellation of existing dipoles by the added adsorbate because of its orientation relative to that already on the surface becomes a possibility. As temperature is raised the ordered arrangement will become less easy to achieve and there will be no occurrence of this phenomenon.

In Section 5-8 reference was made to the unusual result obtained with the HCl-NaCl system, since the water–γ-alumina system also shows a region of the dielectric isotherm in which addition of polarizable matter causes a negligible increase of apparent dielectric constant. That result was obtained when the system was at low temperatures and mobility of the adsorbed matter would be small. The creation of ordered structures with antiparallel dipoles may again be an explanation, but whatever mechanism is ultimately found to account for the observation, the fact has now been established that it may occur for both porous and nonporous adsorbents.

Absolute values of the dielectric constant of the adsorbate ε_2' have been calculated by using the extended Böttcher procedure and the values of liquid-state density at the appropriate temperatures. The first linear regions reveal a dielectric constant of about 27, which is greater than that of bulk liquid at the same temperature, namely, 13.8. However, comparatively little error of the slope can result in this degree of discrepancy, as has already been discussed. The negligible temperature coefficient of the dielectric property is not consistent with the liquid-state value for ε_2', and probably this rough agreement in magnitude is meaningless. Some support is given to this view by the calculated value of ε_2' from the second linear section, which turns out to be negative. The arithmetic reason for this was given in Section 5-3 and suggests that, either because of assumed values of the density of the adsorbate or a failure of the method of calculation, too high values of volume-average polarizability are being obtained.

The transition from the curve representative of the behavior of the system at $-110°C$ to that at $-70°C$ should obviously be more thoroughly traced by reducing the differences of temperature between isotherms. Study of methyl chloride and ethyl chloride on the substrate should also be helpful in obtaining a fuller understanding of the dielectric results.

In conclusion it can be said that the system has shown unexpected complexities which arise because of the interaction between dipoles and which were not taken into account in the theoretical treatment. The importance of dielectric measurements is emphasized, however, for the information supplied by the dielectric isotherms is clearly an important extension of that furnished by the adsorption isotherm.

REFERENCES

1. E. Petrie, Thesis, University of Toronto, 1957.
2. M. Waldman, *Compt. Rend.*, **17**, 426 (1956).
3. J. K. Roberts, "Some Problems in Adsorption" (Cambridge Physical Tracts), Cambridge University Press, New York, 1939.
4. G. C. Benson, E. W. Channen, and R. McIntosh, *J. Colloid Sci.*, **11**, 593 (1956).
5. D. Crozier, Thesis, Queen's University, Kingston, Ontario, Canada, 1965.
6. A. Craig and R. McIntosh, *Can. J. Chem.*, **30**, 448 (1952).
7. D. Young and J. A. Morrison, *J. Sci. Instr.*, **32**, 325 (1955).

APPENDIX A

THE EVALUATION OF ε' AND ε'' FROM THE EXPERIMENTALLY DETERMINED CHARACTERISTICS OF THE STANDING WAVE

Von Hippel (1, 2) develops the equation

$$(\tanh \gamma_2 d)/\gamma_2 d = (-j\lambda_1/2\pi d)[E_{\min}/E_{\max} - j \tan (2\pi X_0/\lambda_1)]/$$
$$[1 - j(E_{\min}/E_{\max}) \tan (2\pi X_0/\lambda_1)]$$

where γ_2 is the complex propagation factor of the wave in medium 2, d is the thickness of the sample, X_0 its distance from the first minimum of the standing wave, and λ_1 the wavelength in the air part of the guide. The right-hand side may be expressed as $Ce^{-j\zeta}$, where C and ζ are obtained from experimental data. The term $\gamma_2 d$ may be expressed as $Te^{j\tau}$. Charts provided by Von Hippel (1) give values of T and τ for values of C and ζ. Knowing T and τ, we may evaluate ε' and ε'' from the definition of γ_2 and the relations which thus exist, namely

$$\varepsilon' = -KT^2 \cos 2\tau$$

$$\varepsilon'' = KT^2 \sin 2\tau$$

where $K = \varepsilon_0 \lambda_1^2/(2\pi d)^2$ and ε_0 is here the dielectric constant of vacuum.

The value of K arises in the following way:

$$\gamma = \alpha + j\beta = j\omega(\varepsilon\mu)^{1/2}$$

where α is the attenuation factor and β the phase factor of the standing wave. In the coaxial-line system, where the air part of the guide is designated as medium 1 and the dielectric as medium 2,

$$z_1 = (\mu_1/\varepsilon_1)^{1/2} \qquad \text{and} \qquad z_1\gamma_1 = j\omega\mu_1$$

Similarly,

$$z_2\gamma_2 = j\omega\mu_2$$

and for nonmagnetic materials this means

$$z_1\gamma_1 = z_2\gamma_2$$

$$\gamma_2^2/\gamma_1^2 = \varepsilon_2/\varepsilon_1$$

For medium 1, assumed lossless,

$$\gamma_1 = j\beta_1 = j2\pi/\lambda_1$$

and

$$\varepsilon_1 = \varepsilon_1' = \varepsilon_0$$

Hence

$$\varepsilon_2 = - \gamma_2^2 \lambda_1^2 \varepsilon_0 / 4\pi^2$$

Since we have defined

$$\gamma_2 d = T e^{j\tau}$$

$$\gamma_2^2 = T^2 (\cos 2\tau + j \sin 2\tau)/d^2$$

so that

$$\varepsilon_2 = - \lambda_1^2 \varepsilon_0 \, T^2 (\cos 2\tau + j \sin 2\tau)/(2\pi d)^2$$

and

$$K = \lambda_1^2 \varepsilon_0 / (2\pi d)^2$$

Because of the forms of the functions, interpolation between curves on the charts is not always easy, and some accuracy of the primary data is readily lost. A solution may be obtained to the equation below which can be programmed for an IBM 1620 computer.

$$(\tanh T e^{j\tau} - C e^{-j\zeta} T e^{j\tau})^2 = 0$$

Calling

$$\tanh T e^{j\tau} = u + jv \qquad \text{and} \qquad C e^{-j\zeta} T e^{j\tau} = x + jy$$

we wish to solve the equation

$$G = (u - x)^2 + (v - y)^2 = 0$$

where

$$u = \frac{\sinh (2T \cos \tau)}{\cosh (2T \cos \tau) + \cos (2T \sin \tau)}$$

and

$$v = \frac{\sin (2T \sin \tau)}{\cosh (2T \cos \tau) + \cos (2T \sin \tau)}$$

and

$$x = CT[\cos (\tau - \zeta)] \qquad y = CT[\sin (\tau - \zeta)]$$

G is thereby given by the equation

$$G = C^2 T^2 + \frac{\cosh (2T \cos \tau) - \cos (2T \sin \tau)}{\cosh (2T \cos \tau) + \cos (2T \sin \tau)}$$

$$- 2CT \frac{[\cos (\tau - \zeta) \sinh (2T \cos \tau) + \sin (\tau - \zeta) \sin (2T \sin \tau)]}{\cosh (2T \cos \tau) + \cos (2T \sin \tau)}$$

Since any values other than the best ones cause the function G to increase, it is assumed that the function can be represented as a paraboloid of the form

$$G = A(T - T_0)^2 + B(T - T_0)(\tau - \tau_0) + D(\tau - \tau_0)^2$$

near the values T_0 and τ_0 which are the best values of the solution of the equation. The quantities A, B, D may be eliminated and T_0 and τ_0 evaluated through the relations

$$\tau_0 = \tau - \left(\frac{\partial^2 G}{\partial T \, \partial \tau} \frac{\partial G}{\partial T} - \frac{\partial^2 G}{\partial T^2} \frac{\partial G}{\partial \tau} \right) \Big/ \left[\left(\frac{\partial^2 G}{\partial T \, \partial \tau} \right)^2 - \frac{\partial^2 G}{\partial \tau^2} \frac{\partial^2 G}{\partial T^2} \right]$$

$$T_0 = T - \left(\frac{\partial^2 G}{\partial T \, \partial \tau} \frac{\partial G}{\partial \tau} - \frac{\partial^2 G}{\partial \tau^2} \frac{\partial G}{\partial T} \right) \Big/ \left[\left(\frac{\partial^2 G}{\partial T \, \partial \tau} \right)^2 - \frac{\partial^2 G}{\partial \tau^2} \frac{\partial^2 G}{\partial T^2} \right]$$

Preliminary values of T and τ are read from the charts and first values of τ_0 and T_0 obtained. The process is repeated until values of τ_0 and T_0 within acceptable limits of the answer are obtained.

Analytical expressions for the first and second derivatives of the function G are very cumbersome. An attempt to obtain a solution by approximating these derivatives through small increments in the G function due to small increments in τ and T was not successful, as the computer gave answers which oscillated in value. It thus became mandatory to employ the exact functions for these terms, and these are given in Table A-1.

REFERENCES

1. A. Von Hippel, "Dielectric Materials and Applications," M.I.T. Press, Cambridge, Mass., and Wiley, New York, 1954.
2. A. Von Hippel, "Dielectrics and Waves," Wiley, New York, 1954.

TABLE A-1 Derivatives of the Function G with Respect to T and τ

$$\frac{\partial G}{\partial T} = [4(AD) - 2C(AX)(AA) - 4CT(AB)]\frac{1}{(AA)^2} + 2C^2T$$

$$\frac{\partial G}{\partial \tau} = [4T(AE) - 2CT(AF)(AA) + 4CT^2(AC)]\frac{1}{(AA)^2}$$

$$\frac{\partial^2 G}{\partial T\,\partial \tau} = [4(AE)(AA) - 2C(AF)(AA)^2 - 8T[\sin Q \sinh P(AA) - 2(AD)(AG)]$$
$$+ 4CT(AC)(AA) - 8CT^2[-(AZ)(AA) + 2(AB)(AG)]]\frac{1}{(AA)^3}$$

$$\frac{\partial^2 G}{\partial T^2} = [8(\cos Q \cosh P)(AA) - 16(AD)(AH) - 8C(AB)(AA)$$
$$- 8CT[(AY)(AA) - 2(AB)(AH)]]\frac{1}{(AA)^3} + 2C^2$$

$$\frac{\partial^2 G}{\partial \tau^2} = [-4T(AD)(AA) + 8T^2[\cos Q \cosh P(AA) + 2(AE)(AG)] + 2CT(AX)(AA)^2 - 4CT^2(AB)(AA)$$
$$- 8CT^3[(AY)(AA) - 2(AC)(AG)]]\frac{1}{(AA)^3}$$

$(AA) = (\cosh P + \cos Q)$

$(AC) = (\sin Z + \sin Z \cos Q \cosh P - \cos Z \sin Q \sinh P)$

$(AD) = (\sin \tau \sin Q \cosh P + \cos \tau \cos Q \sinh P)$

$(AE) = (\cos \tau \sin Q \cosh P - \sin \tau \cos Q \sinh P)$

$(AF) = (\sin Q \cos R - \sin R \sinh P)$

$(AH) = (\cos \tau \sinh P - \sin \tau \sin Q)$

$(AB) = (\cos Z + \cos Z \cos Q \cosh P + \sin Z \sin Q \sinh P)$

$(AG) = (\sin \tau \sinh P + \cos \tau \sin Q)$

$(AX) = (\sin Q \sin R + \cos R \sinh P)$

$(AY) = (\cos R \cos Q \sinh P - \sin R \sin Q \cosh P)$

$(AZ) = (\cos R \sin Q \cosh P + \sin R \cos Q \sinh P)$

where $P = 2T \cos \tau$ $Q = 2T \sin \tau$ $R = \tau - \zeta$

CONTRIBUTION OF A RIGID DIPOLAR MOLECULE TO THE ORIENTATIONAL POLARIZATION WHEN CONSTRAINED TO UNDERGO ROTATIONAL OSCILLATIONS IN A PLANE

A nonpolarizable dipole of moment μ is constrained to make rotational simple harmonic oscillations in the xy plane about an equilibrium position taken as the x axis. The molecule has a moment of inertia I and angular frequency ω_0. Let γ be the angle made with its equilibrium position: $u = \frac{1}{2}I\omega_0^2\gamma^2$ is its potential energy.

An applied field E makes polar angles θ and ϕ with the axes as shown in Figure B-1. The energy of the dipole in the field is

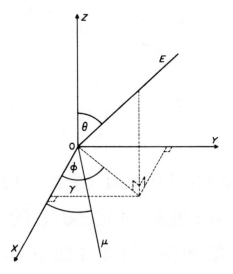

Figure B-1

Representation of a rigid dipole μ relative to the field E and its equilibrium position along the X axis, which would be its orientation when no field is applied.

$-\mathbf{\mu \cdot E}$. E_n and E_p are the component normal to the plane of oscillation and the component parallel to the plane. With the aid of Figure B-1 it is seen that

$$\mathbf{\mu \cdot E} = \mu E \cos{(\phi - \gamma)} \sin{\theta} \qquad \text{(B-1)}$$

The moment of the dipole in the direction of the field is

$$\mathbf{\mu \cdot E}/E = \mu \cos{(\phi - \gamma)} \sin{\theta} \qquad \text{(B-2)}$$

Therefore the average moment in the direction of the field of molecules for which the equilibrium position makes the polar angles θ and ϕ with the field is

$$\bar{m} = \frac{\int_{-\pi}^{\pi} \mu \cos(\phi - \gamma) \sin \theta \exp(-\beta^2 \gamma^2) \exp[\alpha \cos(\phi - \gamma) \sin \theta] \, d\gamma}{\int_{-\pi}^{\pi} \exp(-\beta^2 \gamma^2) \exp[\alpha \cos(\phi - \gamma) \sin \theta] \, d\gamma} \quad \text{(B-3)}$$

where $\beta^2 = I\omega_0^2/2kT$ and $\alpha = \mu E/kT$ and only potential-energy terms are considered. Extension of the limits of integration to plus and minus infinity does not cause appreciable error provided that $\beta^2 \geqslant 0.1$. For small applied fields α is small, and if that exponential term is expanded and the first two terms of the power series retained, there results

$$m_{\theta,\phi} = \frac{\mu \sin \theta \int_{-\infty}^{\infty} \cos(\phi - \gamma)[1 + \alpha \cos(\phi - \gamma) \sin \theta] \exp(-\beta^2 \gamma^2) \, d\gamma}{\int_{-\infty}^{\infty} [1 + \alpha \cos(\phi - \gamma) \sin \theta] \exp(-\beta^2 \gamma^2) \, d\gamma} \quad \text{(B-4)}$$

The integrals resulting are as follows:

$$\int_{-\infty}^{\infty} \exp(-\beta^2 \gamma^2) \, d\gamma = \sqrt{\pi}/\beta$$

$$\int_{-\infty}^{\infty} \cos(\phi - \gamma) \exp(-\beta^2 \gamma^2) \, d\gamma = \cos \phi (\sqrt{\pi}/\beta) \exp(-1/4\beta^2)$$

$$\int_{-\infty}^{\infty} \cos^2(\phi - \gamma) \exp(-\beta^2 \gamma^2) \, d\gamma = (\sqrt{\pi}/2\beta)[\cos 2\phi \exp(-1/\beta^2) + 1]$$

Substituting in Equation (B-4), we obtain

$$\bar{m}_{\theta,\phi} = \frac{\mu \exp(-1/4\beta^2) \sin \theta \cos \phi + \tfrac{1}{2}\alpha\mu \exp(-1/\beta^2) \sin^2 \theta \cos 2\phi + \tfrac{1}{2}\alpha\mu \sin^2 \theta}{1 + \alpha \exp(-1/4\beta^2) \sin \theta \cos \phi}$$

To obtain $\bar{m}$, the average contribution of a molecule for all directions of the field relative to the plane, we have

$$\bar{m} = \int_0^\pi d\theta \int_0^{2\pi} \bar{m}_{\theta,\phi} \sin \theta \, d\phi \Big/ \int_0^\pi d\theta \int_0^{2\pi} \sin \theta \, d\phi$$

Inserting the value of $\bar{m}_{\phi,\theta}$ into this expression and making the approximation $1/(1 + x) \simeq 1 - x$, after integration,

$$\bar{m} = (\alpha\mu/3)[1 - \exp(-1/2\beta^2)] = (\alpha\mu/3)[(1/2\beta^2) - (1/8\beta^4)....]$$

THE EFFECT OF AN ELECTRICAL FIELD
ON THE ENTROPY OF A DIELECTRIC

Fröhlich (1) discusses the effect of an applied field upon the entropy of a dielectric. The influence arises because the energy per unit volume of a dielectric is increased if the dielectric displacement D is increased. For a system of fixed volume the combined first and second laws lead to

$$dU = T \, dS + (E/4\pi) \, dD \qquad \text{(C-1)}$$

where U is the energy per unit volume and where

$$dD = d(\varepsilon_s E) = \varepsilon_s\, dE + E\, d\varepsilon_s$$

It is then considered that the state of the dielectric is determined by the independent variables T and E^2, and thus

$$dS = \left(\frac{\partial S}{\partial T}\right) dT + \left[\frac{\partial S}{\partial (E^2)}\right] d(E^2)$$

and

$$dU = \left(\frac{\partial U}{\partial T}\right) dT + \left[\frac{\partial U}{\partial (E^2)}\right] d(E^2)$$

so that

$$dS = \frac{1}{T}\left(\frac{\partial U}{\partial T} - \frac{E^2}{4\pi}\frac{\partial \varepsilon_s}{\partial T}\right) dT + \frac{1}{T}\left[\frac{\partial U}{\partial (E^2)} - \frac{\varepsilon_s}{8\pi}\right] d(E^2)$$

But since dS is a perfect differential, it follows that

$$\frac{\partial}{\partial (E^2)}\left[\frac{1}{T}\left(\frac{\partial U}{\partial T} - \frac{E^2}{4\pi}\frac{\partial \varepsilon_s}{\partial T}\right)\right] = \frac{\partial}{\partial T}\left[\frac{1}{T}\left(\frac{\partial U}{\partial (E^2)}\right) - \frac{\varepsilon_s}{8\pi}\right]$$

and

$$\frac{\partial U}{\partial (E^2)} = \frac{1}{8\pi}\left(\varepsilon_s + T\frac{\partial \varepsilon_s}{\partial T}\right)$$

On integration with respect to E^2, one obtains

$$U = U_0(T) + \frac{1}{8\pi}\left(\varepsilon_s + T\frac{\partial \varepsilon_s}{\partial T}\right) E^2$$

Now, since

$$\frac{\partial S}{\partial (E^2)} = \frac{1}{T}\left\{\left[\frac{\partial U}{\partial (E^2)}\right] - \frac{\varepsilon_s}{8\pi}\right\} \quad \text{and} \quad \frac{\partial U}{\partial (E^2)} = \frac{1}{8\pi}\left(\varepsilon_s + T\frac{\partial \varepsilon_s}{\partial T}\right)$$

it follows that

$$\frac{\partial S}{\partial (E^2)} = \frac{1}{8\pi}\frac{\partial \varepsilon_s}{\partial T}$$

and finally that

$$S = S_0(T) + \frac{E^2}{8\pi} \frac{\partial \varepsilon_s}{\partial T}$$

Thus, if $\partial \varepsilon_s / \partial T < 0$, the field reduces the entropy, and if $\partial \varepsilon_s / \partial T > 0$, application of the field increases the entropy.

In the case of dielectrics which exhibit loss in the frequency and temperature range of interest an irreversible process is occurring due to the absorption of energy from the field at some temperature $T + \delta T$ and its elimination to the thermostat at T. The amount of energy absorbed per second is given by the imaginary part of $(1/t) \int_0^t E \, dD$, where both E and D are complex. The real part of the expression represents energy stored in the dielectric and returned to the field twice during each cycle.

In spite of the generation of entropy through the irreversible process, the condition of the dielectric is still specified by its temperature, assumed to be T, and by the time average of its polarization. The latter is a function of the applied field at fixed frequency. For unit volume of dielectric we may write the equation analogous to (C-1):

$$dU = T \, dS + (1/4\pi) \, \overline{\text{r.p.} \, E \, dD} \qquad \text{(C-2)}$$

where S is a function of T and the real part of the applied field and D is a function of temperature only at fixed frequency. The bar denotes the time-average value and r.p. the real part of the expression. Again, since $D = \varepsilon E$, $dD = \varepsilon \, dE + E \, d\varepsilon$. Magnitudes are employed since the vectors are parallel.

Substituting into Equation (C-2), and using E^2 as the variable

$$dU = \left(T \frac{\partial S}{\partial T} + \frac{1}{4\pi} \overline{\text{r.p.} \, E^2 \frac{\partial \varepsilon}{\partial T}} \right) dT + \left(T \frac{\partial S}{\partial \bar{E}^2} + \frac{1}{8\pi} \overline{\text{r.p.} \, \varepsilon} \right) d\bar{E}^2$$

Since dU is a perfect differential,

$$\frac{\partial}{\partial \bar{E}^2} \left(T \frac{\partial S}{\partial T} + \frac{1}{4\pi} \overline{\text{r.p.} \, E^2 \frac{\partial \varepsilon}{\partial T}} \right) = \frac{\partial}{\partial T} \left(T \frac{\partial S}{\partial \bar{E}^2} + \frac{1}{8\pi} \overline{\text{r.p.} \, \varepsilon} \right)$$

After integration with ε independent of $\bar{E}^2$, and on evaluation of the time average of the real part of the square of the complex field from the relation

$$\frac{1}{t} \int_0^t \text{r.p. } E^2 \, dt = \frac{E_0^2}{2t} \int_0^t (\cos \omega t + j \sin \omega t)(\cos \omega t - j \sin \omega t) \, dt$$

$$= E_0^2/2$$

one obtains

$$S = S_0(T) + \frac{1}{16\pi} E_0^2 \frac{\partial \varepsilon'}{\partial T}$$

where E_0 is the maximum amplitude of the field. It therefore appears that, as in the case of static fields, the system gains or loses entropy in the presence of a field as the sign of $\partial \varepsilon'/\partial T$ dictates.

REFERENCES

1. H. Fröhlich, "Theory of Dielectrics: Dielectric Constants and Dielectric Loss," pp. 9ff., Clarendon Press, Oxford, 1949.

AUTHOR INDEX

Numbers in parentheses are reference numbers and indicate that an author's work is referred to although his name is not cited in the text. Numbers in italics give the page on which the complete reference is listed.

SUBJECT INDEX

A

Acetone, 65
Actigel, 128
Activation energy
  for ammonia–porous glass systems,
    82–84, 92
  for ethanol and methanol on cellulose,
    113
  for ethyl chloride–porous glass sys-
    tems, 88
    for ethyl chloride–silica gel
    systems, 96
  for starch–water systems, 114, 115
  for water–silica gel systems, 71, 96
  for water on terylene, 112
Additivity
  of dielectric constants, 14, 15, 64
  of internal fields, 12
  of polarization, 11, 13, 20, 21
Admittance, 51
Alumina gel, 90, 98
γ–Alumina, 101, 107, 135
Ammonia,
  on nonporous rutile, 124
  on porous glass, 77–84
  on silica gel, 96
Attenuation factor, 51, 140, 147

B

BET equation, 40, 66, 124
Böttcher's formulas, 20
Bottleneck theory, 97
Bovine serum albumin, 116, 118
Butane
  dielectric constant of, 65, 68, 73
  on nonporous rutile, 122, 131
  on silica gel, 64, 94, 96

C

Capacity increments
  for ammonia–porous glass system, 77,
    79
  for hydrogen chloride on nonporous
    sodium chloride, 133
  for polar adsorbates on silica gel, 98
  variation with quantity adsorbed
    and with temperature, 62
Capillary condensation, 63, 67, 93,
  97, 98
β-Casein, 116
Cellulose, 61, 112
Chemisorbed hydroxyl groups, 56, 73,
  79
  in ammonia–porous glass system, 81,
    84
  elimination of, 57, 85
  on silica gel, 94
  on terylene, 112
Clausius-Mosotti relation, 4, 15, 17
Clusters, 14, 15, 71
Coaxial lines, 46–51, 140
Cole-Cole semicircular plot, 34
Conductance, 116

D

Debye curves, 33, 36, 38
Debye equations, 4, 7, 26–30, 32
Debye-type absorption, 39, 76
Decay function, 8, 26, 30, 34, 37
Deuterated ammonia, 57, 83
Dichlorofluoromethane, 126, 133
Dielectric constant, 4, 68, 71, 73, 122
  real and imaginary parts, 34, 35,
    51, 88
  static, 32. 35, 36, 77

157